A GIFT FOR:

_____

FROM:

_____

With Contributions From:

Jean Thomason

Lisa Harper

Stephanie Lind

Carla Baker

Helen Heavirland

Noni Beth Gibbs

Betty Kossick

Terri Cruze

Linda Nordyke Hambleton

Table *of* Contents

Welcome

Since the dawn of time our human race has been blessed with good gifts. According to ancient Scripture, the Creator made this wondrous world with an astonishing array of plant and animal life. In the center of it all, He created a garden called Eden as a gift for his first two children, Adam and Eve. Along with their garden home, one of the finest gifts God gave the new couple was abundant health. Health in mind, body, and spirit, and a healthy relationship with one another and their world.

By examining the creation story and the Eden environment, we can learn much about feeling fit, living long, and finding peace in our lives today. In fact, after reading and re-reading the remarkable story of earth's establishment in the Book of Genesis, a team of healthcare visionaries chose to use the word CREATION as an easy-to-remember acronym that summarizes the principles of whole-person health. The letters stand for:

These principles of wellness are timeless. Though the perfect Eden environment has been lost and we now live in a world broken by disease, suffering, and death, these principles still have the power to transform lives. By putting

C CHOICE

R REST

E ENVIRONMENT

A ACTIVITY

T TRUST

I INTERPERSONAL RELATIONSHIPS

O OUTLOOK

N NUTRITION

them into practice, you can start your journey toward optimal health and happiness today.

This book is designed help you along your life journey through the power of simple stories. Each story addresses some aspect of healthy living from a mind/body/spirit perspective.

Now, everyone loves a good story. Some stories make us laugh, some cry. Some stories inspire and some make us think. Some stories make us want to sing, others to pray. But they all remind us that as human beings we share far more than similar genes; we are also connected at the heart by our hopes and dreams, joys and faith.

In the pages ahead you'll find simple stories about living life to the full no matter what circumstances come your way. You'll meet women who have faced difficulties such as chronic illness, sudden loss, disaster – those events that only faith can carry us through and that only God has the power to transform into good. You'll also find lessons from nature. Illustrations of how God can touch us through the lilies of the field, the beauty of a sunset, or a hushed walk down a forest trail. Through shared stories we often see how God orchestrates the events of our lives for our instruction, encouragement, and enjoyment.

May these stories build your trust in God and deepen your faith in the love of your Heavenly Father.

Here's To Your Good Health,
Todd Chobotar
Publisher and Editor-in-Chief

The Gift

MARY KENDALL

*A*ll eyes were on me as I stood uncomfortably before a crowd of nearly 5,000 people. I was waiting to open the simply wrapped gift my new friend, Justine, was presenting to me, and the crowd was waiting for my response. I was touched by Justine's thoughtfulness and hopeful that, though I couldn't communicate my appreciation in words, my face would express my gratitude.

I was in Rwanda, Africa. My husband and I were at the conclusion of a three week mission trip. Every day, he had preached and I had given simple health lectures—both with the help of a translator. For three weeks, we had bumped and jolted our way down rutted, dusty roads passing fields where women with babies on their backs worked tirelessly. For three weeks, we'd passed drab, grass huts where nearly naked children played in dirt "yards." For three weeks, we had met daily with this crowd of people, many of whom had walked for several hours to be there and would walk several hours home in the dark. We had seen people who earned less than $1 a month and had worn the same, tattered clothes night after night drop money into the offering basket to help those less fortunate than themselves. We had heard choirs, singing songs about Jesus and the eternal home he's preparing for his children. And night after night, we had seen the joyful faces of people giving their hearts to Jesus for

Justine pressed a scrap of paper into my hand. It read, "To the one who has him, Jesus is everything."

11

the first time as they responded to the invitations. And now this was our final gathering.

Justine had been my friend since we had laid eyes on each other. She was the first to eagerly welcome me with a hug and a smile. I looked for her every night, and every night she was waiting for me. Since we couldn't communicate due to the language barrier, we smiled a lot. Sometimes she led me through the crowd, introducing me to her family and friends. I showed her pictures of my family. Sometimes we sat together and listened to the choirs. Justine sang along, and when I recognized the tune, I sang with her. Although we spoke different languages and lived in vastly different worlds, we shared a special bond.

And now standing here listening as she spoke to the crowd and to me, I thought about how much I would miss her and her easy smile and warm hug. I thought about the "house" she would go home to and my house back in America. I thought about her tattered clothes and the clothes I was wearing—different clothes every day, purchased especially for this trip. I thought about the simple meals that she ate and the endless variety of food I enjoyed at home. I wished so badly to be able to share some of these things with her—things that would undoubtedly make her life easier,

"Therefore it is also contained in the Scripture, 'Behold, I lay in Zion a chief cornerstone, elect, precious, and he who believes on Him will by no means be put to shame.'"

1 PETER 2:6, NKJV.

I thought. Yet in the face of her striking poverty, I could see peace and contentment in Justine's eyes. I thought about my struggle for contentment amidst bounty.

Justine handed me her gift. "Just something so you'll remember her," the translator said. I opened the gift and found a hand woven banner inside. It was made from dried banana leaves and had black letters painted on it. I didn't know what it said, but I was touched that she had thought of me, that she had made something for me. I thanked her and smiled and assured her that I would not forget her. I wished I had a gift for her. I wished I didn't have to leave her behind—with so little.

We said tearful goodbyes and promised that we would meet again—if not on this earth then in the home Jesus is preparing. As my husband and I made our way toward our car and our final journey down the rutted, African roads, Justine came close and pressed a scrap of paper into my hand. It was just a few words: her simple, living testimony, the hand-written translation of the banner she had given me. Tears spilled down my cheeks as I read, "To the one who has him, Jesus is everything."

Love Heals

Dorothy L. Brown

$\mathcal{E}$ach day as I entered the nursing unit I would see him standing at the end of the "V" in the hallway, his bright blue eyes sparkling as he managed a weak smile. His eyes were the bluest I'd ever seen. It seemed one could drown in that pool of blue, but for all their sparkle his eyes were filled with a deep sadness. He was in his mid seventies, so I suspected he had experienced a lot of sadness in his life. He always had a large Bible in his possession, and would cry whenever we talked.

It was a busy, locked mental health unit and I'd only read the pertinent information in his chart. He had been admitted for depression. The oral report received at the beginning of the shift didn't give much information either, except that he remained quiet and depressed. Even for a man in his seventies he was handsome, and it seemed those beautiful blue eyes could swallow you whole. One son was in the Air Force and visited often. He had another son, younger, who was in prison. I felt sure that must be part of the reason for his sadness.

Being of African American heritage it was not unusual to experience prejudice from some of the patients in my care, even from

"But I say unto you, Love your enemies, bless them that curse you, do good to them that hate you, and pray for them which despitefully use you and persecute you..."

MATTHEW 5:44 KJV.

the mentally ill, so it was welcome relief to care for someone who appeared to appreciate me. I was not on duty when he was initially admitted, so I missed the historical report. He received me without prejudice so I didn't mind that the charge nurse daily assigned me to be his nurse.

One day as I tried to get him to open up he said to me, "I've done a lot of bad things in my life, really bad things. I ruined my son's life and he's in jail, and the people I've hurt the most have been the kindest to me." My heart went out to him and I held his hands in mine as I prayed for God to give him peace. He cried.

I spoke to the other nurses about his despair and one said to me, "Don't you know who your patient is? He's the Grand Dragon of the Ku Klux Klan!" I was stunned! That sweet man, those blue eyes. He was going to be tried for his past crimes. Still, my heart went out to him, for I sensed his deep remorse, and I passed no judgment on him. I thought no judgment or punishment was worse than the sentence he had placed upon himself. It seems my kindness to him must have been ripping away at his heart. I did not mention the KKK to him, and continued to comfort and care for him as before. His anguish was obvious to anyone who took the time to see, and I could not

One of my fellow nurses asked, "Don't you know who your patient is? He's the Grand Dragon of the Ku Klux Klan!"

help but feel empathy for him. I was better able to understand Matthew 5:44: "But I say unto you, Love your enemies, bless them that curse you, do good to them that hate you, and pray for them which despitefully use you and persecute you..." (KJV). It was freeing to me to feel genuine love and compassion for this man who once hated me, sight unseen, but who could not now love himself.

Racial prejudice was present when Jesus walked this earth. In one of his devotionals, Oswald Chambers mentions the animosity and "racial prejudice" of the Samaritans toward Jesus, a Jew. Yet the Lord had one of his best known conversations with a Samaritan woman he met at Jacob's well. He taught his disciples to do good to those who hate you. That was an easy command to obey when I first looked into eyes the color blue of a pristine sea.

Consider
the Lilies

LAURA BRADFORD

*A*s another parched summer day came to an end, I went outside to give my gardens an extra drink of water.

Normally, I'd enjoy those few moments of lingering in the twilight, but worries about money were weighing me down. I'd just finished reviewing the financial status of my widowed mother-in-law's accounts and my own. With Mom in an expensive Alzheimer's facility, it appeared she'd outlive her money. Since I'm a widow too, I wondered if I'd suffer the same fate. How could I make my money last? Should I quit giving to charity? Quit using the air conditioner? Quit watering the yard?

I knew I couldn't let my gardens die.

In the fading sunset, the colors of my flowers took on a surreal glow. Trees whispered a lullaby, while the cooling breeze embraced me in a gentle caress. How could I let all this wither and die? The very thought broke my heart.

If that is how God clothes the grass of the field, which is here today, and tomorrow is thrown into the fire, how much more will he clothe you, O you of little faith!" LUKE 12:27-28, NIV.

This was my sanctuary—a place to meet with the Lord in the cool of the evening—a place to escape a crazed, self-adoring world, and imagine Eden. Everything here bore the Lord's signature. To quote Paul from Romans

1:20, "God's invisible qualities" (NIV) were displayed in the vast array of colors, in the bountiful crops, even in the crescent moon smiling down at me. Faint chirpings of sleepy birds seemed to confirm, "All is well. God is here." But worries kept me from receiving comfort from their evensong.

Dragging my garden hose to a flowerbed, I swept water over the mass of color. As leaves and petals danced under the droplets, I noticed a few tall leaves parting to reveal a stranger in my garden—a new flower.

"What are you doing here?" I asked, dropping the hose to have a better look.

I stared in disbelief as a pink calla lily swayed gracefully on her stock, like a royal matron, surrounded by her entourage of petunias.

But I hadn't planted a lily there! To me, lilies were a waste of money, blooming only briefly before they shrivel and die. But, there she stood, a tall lady wrapped in a delicate pink cape.

As I gazed in awe, Jesus' own words came to me. "Consider how the lilies grow. They do not labor or spin. Yet I tell you, not even Solomon in all his splendor was dressed like one of these. If that is how God clothes the grass of the field, which is here today, and tomorrow is thrown into the fire, how much more will he clothe you, O you of little faith!" (Luke 12:27-28, NIV).

Joy replaced worry as the truth of those verses soaked into my soul. The miracle lily's silent message convicted me of trusting dollars rather than trusting God! How foolish to doubt the One who'd taken care of me since childhood! He'd always been there, through illnesses, losses, and lean times. He wasn't about to abandon me now.

Tears poured down my face … inching around a smile of relief. Without my asking, without my believing, God had sent a messenger of peace, a sign of his power! If he was capable of planting this lily to bloom exactly when I needed it, wasn't he also capable of meeting every need, at any time, in any form?

A week passed since I had found the lily. She's still stood tall, waving on the breezes. Evidently, she was determined to show off her beauty until I fully understood the Lord's promise, "… *I am with you always, to the very end of the age*" (Matthew 28:20, NIV).

This Race is Not Just for the Runners

MULENGA MUNDENDE

T look forward to spring with great anticipation. Spring brings the beauty of budding trees, sweet-smelling flowers, warm sunshine, and scents of freshly mowed grass. Spring ushers in the time to train outdoors for competitive running races. I have run several half-marathons and 5Ks. I run these races with all my strength, not expecting to win any, but to improve on my previous time, enjoy myself, and cross the finish line.

I developed illotibial band syndrome on both knees when I was training for my second half marathon. I became the poster child for what not to do when training because I did everything wrong. I increased my mileage too fast, did not wear proper shoes, did not rest adequately between runs, stretch properly, or listen to my body. When I ran or walked, I felt excruciating pain that felt as if my knees were being stabbed by a hot, sharp knife. I had never experienced anything like that before. I was forced to halt training two weeks prior to the race.

It was a dark, rainy day when the race started. I was feeling pretty well until the middle of the first mile, when the pain returned, not as excruciating as before, but agonizing enough to slow me down tremen-

"Let us run with endurance the race God has set before us. We do this by keeping our eyes on Jesus, the champion who initiates and perfects our faith"

HEBREWS 12:1-2A, NLT.

dously. The pain removed the fun from the race and shattered my goal of beating my previous time. All I wanted to do then was cross the finish line.

I was challenged mentally and physically. When the pain got worse, I threw myself a pity party. The rain and pain frustrated me. I was not excited about the people who were passing me and running with ease. Wasn't it just easier to stop and call a cab? Then it hit me. Focusing on my pain was not helping matters. I decided to recite one of my favorite Bible verses: "I can do all things through Christ, who gives me strength" (Philippians 4:13, NLT).

As I repeatedly said this verse, something miraculous happened. God gave me strength and opened my heart and eyes. I saw people of different shapes, physical conditions, and nationalities; all running at different levels. Some speed walked, leisurely walked, jogged, or sprinted. I remembered the lyrics from Cindy Morgan's song "Take My Life": "This race is not just for the runners, some of us walk while others barely crawl," and found them to be appropriate, meaningful, and applicable at that moment.

I looked on the sidelines and saw friends, family members, and volunteers who had wo-

> *Focusing on my pain was not helping matters. I decided to recite one of my favorite Bible verses: "I can do all things through Christ, who gives me strength"* PHILIPPIANS 4:13, NLT.

ken up early to cheer us on and provide physical nourishment. Looking around, I saw, as if for the first time, my earthly father who had been running beside me the whole race, cheering me on.

I have often reflected on that experience. I learned that we are in a spiritual race, running at different levels of our spirituality, building relationships with our heavenly Father, while seeking and doing his will as the Holy Spirit convicts us. When life throws different challenges at us we need to cling to God's mighty arms. Surrounded by other men and women, we will do well if we shift the focus from us to them, being their cheerleaders, offering our time, providing an encouraging word, or meeting their physical needs. Most importantly, we should focus our attention on our Savior and Lord. We will do well to remember that our Heavenly Father is with us every step of the way, encouraging, supporting, and carrying us when we cannot go any farther. As the champion of champions, he initiates and perfects our faith. He will see us through to the finish line. If he cannot remove the challenge, he will provide the strength to overcome it.

Seven Years

of Bad....

Seven Years

of Plenty

CYNTHIA MERCER

My morning began like most other days, except this particular day I longed for some answers from God and had decided the night before I would spend the day fasting and praying as I waited on what God wanted to reveal to me. So as I made my way up to the operating room I asked God to put someone in my path that day I could show his love to as well.

That early October morning, it was obvious that my first patient was extremely nervous about her scheduled operation. She had a very familiar face and she seemed to recognize me as well. As we began to visit, we realized that we did know each other from a home school coalition group I had attended earlier in the year. She was very relieved that I was going to be her nurse and she began to cry and express to me her concerns in regard to the surgery she was about to have.

I had just asked her if I could pray for her, when a friend of hers approached the bedside and my patient began to cry even more intensely as she expressed her sadness that her husband wasn't a believer. I sensed she was very hurt, since her tears went beyond the fact that she was having surgery that day.

I asked if I could pray for

As I made my way up to the operating room I asked God to put someone in my path that day I could show his love to.

27

her, and as I prayed it was obvious that she was very burdened down that day. As I said, "Amen," her tears seemed to fade away and she thanked me for the kind words and the prayer.

Immediately following our prayer, the Holy Spirit prompted me to share with her my story about my husband's conversion experience seven years earlier. I explained that when I had married him I was sure I had found the man of my dreams … only to discover a few months later that he was an alcoholic, and addicted to pornography, cocaine, and crystal meth as well. I was extremely distraught and confused. I had two choices, one being to leave and file for a divorce; the other being to stay and pray and watch God perform a miracle! One morning in my quiet time, the Holy Spirit impressed me that if I were to leave I would miss out on the testimony that God wanted to give me. So, I chose to stay and let God have his way with me.

I began to fast and pray for my husband. It wasn't an overnight process and there were many tears and sleepless nights as I agonized in prayer for him. I encouraged her to not give up on praying for her husband. It dawned on me at about the moment I began to pray for her that it had been fourteen years since my husband and I had married and that although the first seven

"Delight thyself also in the Lord: and he shall give thee the desires of thine heart."

PSALM 37:4, KJV.

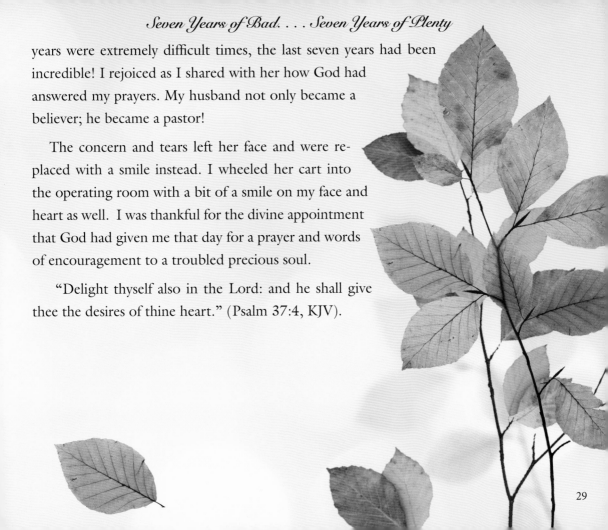

years were extremely difficult times, the last seven years had been incredible! I rejoiced as I shared with her how God had answered my prayers. My husband not only became a believer; he became a pastor!

The concern and tears left her face and were replaced with a smile instead. I wheeled her cart into the operating room with a bit of a smile on my face and heart as well. I was thankful for the divine appointment that God had given me that day for a prayer and words of encouragement to a troubled precious soul.

"Delight thyself also in the Lord: and he shall give thee the desires of thine heart." (Psalm 37:4, KJV).

Waiting for Morning

ALICIA BRUXVOORT

*T*hear the pitter-patter of his sleepy feet before his voice wakes me. I don't need to look at the clock on my bedside table. I know it reads 3 AM. This is his waking time. His squinty eyes and slurred speech confirm that he's not rested, but according to the odd rhythm of my three-year-old son's sleep pattern, daylight should have already arrived.

He tugs at my arm, and asks, "Is it morning yet?"

"No buddy," I whisper, trying not to wake his exhausted daddy beside me. "It's still dark outside."

A shrill moan slips from his lips. "When will morning come?"

"When the darkness disappears," I remind him.

Reluctantly, I roll from bed and grab his slender hand. Like every other night, we walk across the hallway to the room where his big brother sleeps. I nudge my littlest boy into the bottom bunk, pull his special blanket to his chin, and kiss him goodnight again.

"For his anger lasts only a moment, but his favor lasts a lifetime; weeping may remain for a night, but rejoicing comes in the morning" PSALM 30:5, NIV.

"Stay by me and pray for me," he pleads. I glance at my cozy bed across the hall.

"Please, Mommy, just *one* minute." I crawl carefully beside him and place my hands on his

31

head of tousled hair. I breathe in deeply his sleepy smell and remind myself that this child won't be little forever.

"Dear Lord," I murmur so as not to wake my firstborn snoring above us. "Wrap your mighty arms around Joshua. Keep him safe. Command your angels to stand guard over this boy, your treasure..." I speak softly the Scripture that comes to mind. I rub his warm bony back. I listen to the steady pulse of his breathing. I try not to think about my own cramped legs wedged into the crack between his bed and the wall. I whisper assurance that morning will, indeed, arrive. And I empathize with his impatience. No matter how old we grow, it is difficult to wait in darkness.

I've asked my heavenly Father countless times when morning would come. As I've hovered crib–side and listened for the belabored breathing of my struggling newborn; as I've battled mammoth discouragement and wondered if God even cares; as I've listened to the anxious voice on the phone, "Your sister's in the hospital again." Such moments are the nighttimes of the soul. Darkness makes dawn seem so far away.

In her book *Calm My Anxious Heart*, Linda Dillow reminds us that "*faith is walking in the dark with God, holding his hand.*" Savor her insightful commentary on a familiar Bible story. "*In the book of Exodus, we find the children of Israel camped by the edge of the Red Sea. It was night, pitch black except for the pillar of fire God had placed between His people and the Egyptians. Can you imagine their fear?*"

"Hidden in the text is the tiny phrase, 'All that night the LORD drove the sea back' (Exodus 14:21, NIV).... Because it was night, they couldn't see what the 'wind of God' was accomplishing on their behalf.... [But in the morning] they walked on dry ground to freedom."[1]

When we find ourselves in the nighttime of life, we are wise to remember that God is working even when we can't see. Just as he intervened "all that night," for his chosen people while they clung to one another in fear, he is faithfully at work in our darkness, too.

My small son's sluggish snores eventually bring my prayers to a close. Silently, I slip my hands out from under his sleeping head and return to the comforts of my own bed. The sky is still black, but the frogs and the crickets sing a rowdy song of hope beyond my window. They know morning is on its way. Or perhaps they are watching the Creator of the stars work wonders in the darkness.

As for me, I'll have to wait for morning.

[1]Linda Dillow. *Calm My Anxious Heart: A Woman's Guide to Finding Contentment* (Colorado Springs, NavPress, 2007), 151.

Pushing Through Life

STEPHANIE LIND

Some days it feels like all I do is push...

Push the snooze button (okay, twice). Push my way through morning traffic. Push to get more things done in a day. Even push the limits on the minimum amount of sleep time!

Why so much pushing? Society seems to have the view that more is better... So we push.

"...do not be anxious about anything, but in everything by prayer and supplication with thanksgiving let your requests be made known to God. And the peace of God, which surpasses all understanding, will guard your hearts and your minds in Christ Jesus"

PHILIPPIANS 4:6-7, ESV.

One morning as I pushed open an office door, a friend walking through must have seen the stressed look on my face and simply said: "PUSH... Pray Until Something Happens." She just mentioned it casually as the door had PUSH written on the handle bar, but her simple acronym really got me thinking. How often do I push through life, trying to direct my own path and getting frustrated in the process? In reality, I should PUSH as soon as my alarm goes off. I should PUSH for peace during my morning commute. I should PUSH all throughout my day.

I work in a hospital. In this setting, there can be a lot of physical pushing—pushing patients in wheelchairs, pushing life saving medicine through a patients IV, pushing our keyboards while typing up the next great business proposal. And just think of all those women in labor and delivery; there is a lot of pushing in that unit! Each of these pushing opportunities around us can provide a silent reminder to pray. Pray until something happens.

Is there more pushing than peace-of-mind in your life? Perhaps you find yourself pushing day-to-day more than you might wish? You may feel pressured by trying to manage a tight family budget, or balancing the demands of being a loving wife, mother, cook, pet supervisor, house cleaner, charitable volunteer, calendar manager, cheerleader-in-chief, chauffer, and organizer of multiple activities, from Christmas parties to birthday parties, and everything in between. As a result, at the end of many days, there seems to be not enough time or energy for yourself, your spouse, or your relationship with the Lord.

One of my favorite Scripture passages says, "Are you tired? Worn out? Burned out on religion? Come to me. Get away with me and you'll recover your life. I'll show you how to take a real rest. Walk with me and work with me – watch how I do it. Learn the unforced rhythms of grace. I won't lay anything heavy or ill-fitting on you. Keep company with me and you'll learn to live freely and lightly" (Matthew 11:28-30, MSG).

"Learn the unforced rhythms of grace." Unforced. My life is part of God's plan, which is therefore a recipient of unforced, pure grace. If it had a label it would read, "No pushing necessary!" I don't have to try to force things to happen, because he is in charge.

Can you feel the hug from God around you? If God is by my side each step of the way, he will show me how to live "freely and lightly." The burden of having to manage it all is gone. I can "cease striving" and stop pushing and just rest in knowing that he is God. I wonder what would happen if every time we pushed, we PUSHed as well?

The Master Gardener

DIANE THURBER

This spring my gracious neighbors invited me to share garden space with them. I was excited, because gardening in their 10-foot-high fenced-in space promised protection from most critters for my tender plants and developing produce. It also offered four-foot raised beds for gardening ease with timers for automatic watering morning and afternoon, screens to keep the menacing birds away, and a greenhouse with regulated temperature, automatic watering, and classical music to help my plants thrive.

When the *Farmer's Almanac* said it was optimal time to plant, I drove to the amazing, award-winning Tagawa Gardens where master gardeners and gardener-wannabes like me come from near and far to explore 160,000 square feet of heirloom seeds, organic fertilizers that promise to double plant size or yield, and unusual species of vegetables and culinary herbs. In fact, this spring they offered sixteen varieties of garlic!

Soon my shopping cart was loaded with more than I came for – tender plants, seeds, insect spray, string and trellises. I left Tagawa Gardens with increased confidence after coaching and encouragement from their well-educated gardening team.

As I tended my little garden space, I had time to reflect about my Master Gardener who guards and guides the less-than-suitable soil of my heart.

After allowing sufficient time for my delicate plants to adjust from the shaded, protective

39

indoor nursery to their new outdoor environment with piercing sunrays and brisk winds, I lovingly deposited my treasures in the rich garden soil.

I've gardened before, but this year my garden was the most effortless creation I've ever tended. In years past, I toiled over hardened dirt mixed with clay that sprouted weeds of countless varieties to prepare a place to deposit my investment, and each time hoped for a surplus yield. I was often disappointed. But not this year. With optimum soil, well water without chemical additives that soaked the roots, and natural fertilizer from the neighbor's horse stable, I realized I actually did very little to produce the bountiful harvest that included sweet corn, broccoli, lettuce, eggplant, basil, succulent cantaloupe, juicy watermelon, tomatoes, okra, tender peas, and peppers.

As I tended my little garden space, I had time to reflect about my Master Gardener who guards and guides the less-than-suitable soil of my heart. I thought about how he longs to nourish me so I'll lovingly turn to the Son and flourish like my vegetables; but sometimes, I stubbornly cling to selfish ambition like my sugar peas that reach out for nearby veggies instead of the trellis I carefully placed near them for support. The pea plants wrap themselves around the shorter vegetables nearby, and their growth is stunted. I do that sometimes, too, thinking I know a better plan than my Master Gardener. And my growth is stunted. And then I can feel my Master Gardner gently pruning and redirecting my life when I ask him to.

Like the fertilizer I blended with the rich soil to strengthen my little plants, my Master

Gardener longs to enrich me with the nutrients he deposits in his manual for my happiness, the Bible. As I read, I find this book has so many lessons designed to help me grow to my fullest potential as he designed.

And then there's the insect spray. There were so many varieties of bugs and worms just waiting to dine on my endless buffet, and they threatened to reduce the plants to mere stubs. As I did my best to ward off these menacing species, it was sometimes a losing battle. I am thankful for my Master Gardener who never sleeps nor slumbers, who sends his angels to camp round about me to keep me in all my ways. What peace this brings me!

I've learned it's all about trust. My Master Gardner wants me to submit to him, so he can lovingly lead and guide me to be all he dreams for me to be. It's a partnership. He doesn't force me, but when I stray he patiently waits for me to let him be the Master Gardener again. When I encounter unanticipated dangers, he's there to protect. My job is to trust. Simply trust.

The View from 26 Weeks

Jamie Santa Cruz

*W*e are newlyweds, my husband and I, young at love and head over heels for each other. So much so, in fact, that the whiteboard on our refrigerator is still updated each Friday with a fresh count of the number of weeks we've been married. "25" it reads now, but tomorrow, Daniel will rub out that number and replace it with a "26" in fresh black script.

Six months? Has the time really flown so quickly?

We didn't get here easily. In fact, the first time we met, through an introduction by mutual friends three years ago, Daniel was cold to romance. Women were best avoided at all costs, or so his thinking went. We did not keep in touch.

But a year later, when by happenstance we met for the second time, he felt differently. Perhaps it was something about the Christmastime air, but for whatever magical reason, he was interested. This time, phone calls followed. I was intrigued, though unfortunately by then I was just beginning a new relationship with someone else. Again Daniel and I parted ways, but he told me to call if things didn't work out.

Spring came and went, and by June it was clear that indeed, things were not going to work out. I was alone again. Daniel, too, was still alone. Was he still interested? I didn't know, but my tentative phone call yielded a positive response: Yes, he was interested.

"... as a bridegroom rejoices over his bride, so will your God rejoice over you" Isaiah 62:5b, NIV.

Third time's a charm, they say. Somewhere between Christmas and New Years, on a crisp, star-studded evening, he told me that he was going to marry me someday. I giggled. By then, I knew that when he asked, I would say yes.

Our wedding was in May five months later—a simple affair in a beautiful Civil War-era painted white church, at sundown on a Friday evening and with lanterns in the windows. Despite the trials and obstacles that remain constant in life, every day since then has been sweeter than those that came before.

Today, half a year removed from our exchange of vows, I am stirring bean soup at the stove and trying to remember how much chili powder goes into the recipe, when I am jolted from my concentration as Daniel pokes his head into the kitchen.

"Mi amor!" he calls to me, a boyish grin lighting his face. He sweeps into the kitchen, and I can't help laughing as he whisks me off my feet and twirls me around the room. When he sets me back on the floor, he takes my hand and leads me in an impromptu dance, for which neither of us knows the steps. Soon we are tripping over each other's feet and collapsing, laughing and out of breath, into each other's arms.

"Tesoro de mi corazón," he whispers into my ear, drawing my head to his chest. He is teaching me Spanish, his native language, but we joke that his approach is a little impractical for the real world, as my schooling in the romantic vocabulary of the language is far outpacing more usable vocabulary. But never mind that. I know I am loved, and I wouldn't trade that for perfect Spanish fluency.

Entering into this new stage of life with my husband has brought a fresh understanding of what the love of God must be like. After all, in the Bible, it is God who is presented as a bridegroom and we, his people, are the object of his desire, whom he pursues with ardor and tender concern. The authors of both the Old and New Testaments draw on the imagery of the love of a man for a woman as one of the best earthly insights into the intensity of God's passion for his people (e.g. Hosea 1-3; 2 Corinthians 11:2; Revelation 21:2).

Now that I have been a bride, I comprehend this divine love a little better. Every time I fall into my husband's embrace or shiver under the tender touch of his fingers, I sense more clearly the love God feels for me.

And all I can say is this: if the love I share with Daniel is at all comparable to the love God has for us, how sweet must be God's love.

A Worthy Resolution

HELEN HEAVIRLAND

ing-dong.

Tense and tired of interruptions, I trudged toward the door. Treasured out-of-state friends greeted me. My husband heard and hurried from a back room.

The hello's and what's-happening's buzzed back and forth while we and our nature-loving friends drank in the view from our hilltop home. In the few minutes we visited, thirty delicately-designed California quail, topknots bouncing, scratched and pecked at our porch-side bird restaurant. A sparrow hawk surveyed the lower pasture from a fence post. Two bronze-breasted, ring-necked pheasant roosters strutted across the snow. Mallards swam in the stream below. Oregon juncos arrived and flitted and feasted among the quail.

I hadn't seen that many birds in weeks. I started to say so when a hawk soared by just *below* us. We "oohed" and "aahed"—what a treat to look down on the miracle of flight, to see pinions flutter in the updraft, to watch the hawk's head turn from side to side as he sought supper.

One of those "Ah-Hah" moments burst upon me. *You haven't seen many birds lately because you've not sat still and looked*.

Our friends soon continued their journey. My husband went to work. Lost in thought, I laundered and cleaned.

Lately, employment and errands, cooking and cleaning, church-going and bill-paying, family, friends, and crises had demanded my attention. Weeks had appeared and whooshed away at a dizzying pace.

A poster I'd seen popped into mind. Piles of paperwork covered a desktop and overflowed onto the floor. Nearly hidden behind the clutter, a frazzle-haired, bleary-eyed woman stared at the chaos. I could almost hear her drone the caption, "The hurrier I go, the behinder I get."

My own life seemed to overflow the bounds of twenty-four-hour days. Last week had cast its leftovers into yesterday. Yesterday had heaved its unfinished tasks helter-skelter into today.

I thought back to a previous home. Life had pressured and prodded me then as much as now. Perhaps more. But there I'd learned that otters don't schedule appointments to frolic in the river. That rainbows disappear. That gorgeous wood ducks don't ring the doorbell and ask if you want to see them. I'd learned to take minute vacations—to stop and look at a cloud formation, to listen to rain patter or pound the roof, to be cheered by a chickadee at the bird feeder.

I had learned that these pauses to appreciate the common or the spectacular did not decrease my productivity. Instead, minute vacations with the created and the Creator relaxed and energized me. They empowered me to accomplish more. They helped me maintain a peace that improved the quality of life for me . . . and those nearby.

Pressure to do more and be more had crowded out my minute vacations. I didn't know just when I'd allowed it. But I was tired. I dared not wait for rest till some far-off holiday. As I passed an east window, movement in the snow-covered field caught my attention. *What's that?* I wondered.

My momentum moved me on. Then . . . I consciously chose to lay down my armload of clean clothes and get started on a worthy resolution. I fetched binoculars. In the year we'd lived here, we'd observed hundreds of geese fly over but we'd not seen any settle where we could observe them. Now a dozen Canada geese gabbled and fed just a hundred yards from our window.

After just moments of watching nature, I felt refreshed, because I had been reminded to: "Be still and know that I am God..." (Psalm 46:10, KJV).

The Gift
of Choice

DELORES FRANCOIS

*I*t was on a Friday evening in October 1992, when I received the call from my sister, Beverly, that our father had passed way. She wanted to know my plans for the funeral. I told her that I would not be attending. Why in the world would I want to go to the funeral of a stranger? He had abandoned us when we were children and I still remembered the day he left. He had told Beverly and I that he was going away to get a job in another town and that he would return and get us. He never returned.

Beverly always loved our father and I believe she always saw him for who he could have been. I have always liked that about her. Even though he had abandoned us, she chose to love him as if he was always there being the best father there was. Later in life, she would always encourage me to call and say hello to him and let him know what was going on in my life. Sometimes I would. Most times I would not.

My father was an alcoholic. As a child, I remember his friends bringing him home so drunk he literally passed out on the floor. My mother was so frustrated that she kept hitting him with a big wooden stick trying to wake him up. He would not move. I remember thinking that he was dead. How scary of a memory is that for a child! But not all my memories of my father were scary. I can remember running down the street with Beverly to greet him upon his return from

Why in the world would I want to go to the funeral of a stranger?

work each evening. He would pick the both of us up at the same time and hug us!

My father's absence affected our family deeply. He had left us so vulnerable. There were so many things that happened in my life that I attribute to him not being there. The one thing that stands out most in my mind was the strangers who came in and out of our lives, taking advantage of my mom and silently hurting her children, especially her daughters. We were changed undeniably forever because of it. We bear the deep scars; some hidden and some not so hidden.

God in his divine wisdom gave each of us the power of choice. My father and our family suffered the consequences of his choices. I certainly have made choices in my life that I am not proud of. They have affected me and others. Most importantly, I realize that my choices have eternal consequences. I am so happy that God forgives us when we make bad decisions. It is my earnest prayer that God will direct me as I strive to do better with the choices I make each day.

Two days after Beverly's call, I changed my mind and made the choice to attend my father's funeral. I am so happy I did! After all, he was my father and the only one I had in this world. Beverly and I were the only two out of our six siblings who attended. We learned from relatives who cared for him during his illness that in his heart he had never abandoned us. He spoke of us often and

Today, I choose to remember how much my father loved me. I choose to forgive and not to live with bitterness.

shared his memories of us over and over again. It meant so much to us to know that!

It has been eighteen years since my father's death. When I speak of him, even today, it brings tears to my eyes and I feel like a little girl again wanting my father to sweep me up in his arms again! Today, I choose to remember how much my father loved me. I choose to forgive and not to live with bitterness.

Choice is a power and a privilege our heavenly Father has given all of us. What will you do with yours?

"All the paths of the Lord are mercy and truth unto such as keep his covenant and his testimonies. For thy name's sake, O Lord, pardon mine iniquity; for it is great. What man is he that feareth the Lord? him shall he teach in the way that he shall choose. His soul shall dwell at ease; and his seed shall inherit the earth" (Psalm 25: 10-13, KJV).

Somersaults in the Sky

TERRI CRUZE

I love to go hiking! At the mere mention of the word, I almost begin to drool as I run for my shoes: "A hike? When? Where? What are we waiting for? Let's go!" I feel so close to God, so connected to life, when I am hiking. It isn't that I think God is any closer to me on a hike; it's more like I'm less distracted and more tuned-in to his presence, and my heart is more available to his touch.

When I am at home or at work, I tend to focus on the minute details of the tasks before me. A thousand things run through my head all at the same time, like a whirlwind: *What did I leave unfinished yesterday? What am I going to make for dinner? Don't forget to stop at the store and pick up some bread and milk. Did I tell my family that I love them before I left this morning?*

As I stood watching them tumble and soar, I couldn't help feeling a little more light-hearted myself. I felt joy growing inside me as I watched them and imagined myself joining them.

When I am out in the woods or up on a mountain, however, I leave the distractions behind. I am there, alone with God, with the evidence of his love, his beauty, and his creativity all around me. I can't get enough of it! I guess I am a hike-a-holic—but it works for me.

One particular afternoon hike stands out in my mind: I

was out with my kids and a few friends on one of the mountains near my home in the Pacific Northwest. It was a bit windy that day, but the sun was out, and the sky was clear. The views from the ridge we were following were breathtaking! I was just imagining what we would be able to see when we got to the top —probably twenty miles in any direction from that lofty vantage point—when suddenly, something to our left grabbed my attention. What caught my eye was a group of about eight or ten large, black birds, vultures I thought, several hundred feet above a cliff. I was intrigued by what they were doing.

They were lined up in a row at the top of the cliff, and, one at a time, they were falling forward into the wind and performing all kinds of aerobatic flips and dives and somersaults in the air. Of course, it is not unusual for birds to dive and circle around in the sky, but these birds just seemed to be having so much fun doing it! They weren't searching for food or following a migration path. They weren't working at all, as far as I could tell. They were just taking time off and enjoying themselves.

I must admit, for a moment I was a bit envious. But as I stood watching them tumble and soar, I couldn't help feeling a little more light-hearted myself. I felt joy growing inside me as I watched them and imagined myself joining them. How exhilarating the wind must feel rushing by as they dove over the edge, their wings catching the air just right and sending them flying back up, high above the cliff. How free they must feel! As I left them and continued with my own journey, I began to walk with a little more spring in my step and inhaled a little deeper.

The Spirit moved me to wonder: *Is this how my heavenly Father feels when he sees me fully experiencing life? Does he put his arm around my shoulder and say, "Yes! That's it! Go ahead, have fun. Take it all in! I made this for you; do you like it?"*

Then it hit me! This is what Jesus must have meant when he said, *"...I have come that they may have life, and have it to the full" (John 10:10, NIV)*. He did not tell us that if we are good enough, or if we somehow qualified, he would send a select few of us a special blessing of joy. No, he was very clear that he came to give each of us an abundant, joyful life. We can have it, right here and right now. No strings attached, if we simply accept it. What an awesome gift!

Never More *than* *You Can* *Handle*

SHARON JALLAD

*W*hen the phone rang late one evening in 2007 and my father's home number flashed on the caller ID, my immediate response was a mix of anxiety and dread. A phone call from his night nurse usually meant that something was wrong. My experience after six years of being my father's legal guardian told me it could be a number of urgent things—either Dad had fallen again, his blood pressure was too high, or he was out of diapers. While I knew that I could not and would not ignore the ringing plea for assistance, there were times when the phone rang that I wished to escape. Like many women, I found myself stretched between being a wife, a mother of two children, a full-time insurance executive, and caring for my infirm father.

As I feared, the dreaded phone call that night turned out to be more serious than a request for adult diapers. Dad was prone to falling. He had suffered a debilitating stroke in 2003 which left him paralyzed on his right side and aphasic. His limited mobility was shaky at best even when supported by the arms of caregivers and a sturdy cane. Always determined, however, to flex some independence, on that night, Dad had attempted to walk without assistance to the bathroom and had fallen backward, splitting his head open on the sharp corner of a bookcase.

God is faithful. He will not allow the temptation to be more than you can stand. When you are tempted, he will show you a way out so that you can endure"

1 CORINTHIANS 10:13, NLT.

Thank God for 911 and first responders!

After reciting from memory a list of current medications and my father's medical history over the phone to the paramedics, I nervously agreed to meet the ambulance at the hospital's emergency room. Visits to the hospital had become as routine as getting the kids off to school—grab a sweater, a book, a snack, and my cell phone. I knew the drill well and prepared for the long hours ahead.

After a marathon night of medical forms, tests and uncertainty, the doctors admitted my father for further treatment. The sun was coming up and the night shift headed off-duty, when I finally wandered sleepily to the parking lot. In the quiet of my car, overcome by fatigue and worry, I began to cry. *How could I continue to care for my father and juggle the rest of my life?* I wondered. I was not sure I had the strength or the courage. Then, as I was driving home, a strange sense of release came over me and I realized that I was exactly where I was supposed to be in my life, that God had put me in that place so that I could give my father the care that he needed.

I had a loving husband who gave me support.

I had a job that allowed me flexible time-off.

In the quiet of my car, overcome by fatigue and worry, I began to cry. How could I continue to care for my father and juggle the rest of my life?

I was blessed with good health to sustain me.

My father passed away in December 2007. The responsibility of caring for him, while never easy, opened my heart and blessed my life in so many unexpected ways. I cherish the time I spent with him and the love that bound us especially during the most difficult moments of his declining health. The journey was emotionally and physically exhausting, but along the way I continued to be comforted in knowing that God knew in advance what would be required of me and how much I could handle.

"The temptations in your life are no different from what others experience. And God is faithful. He will not allow the temptation to be more than you can stand. When you are tempted, he will show you a way out so that you can endure" *(1 Corinthians 10:13, NLT).*

Perfectly Planned

LIZBETH FERNANDEZ

All little girls dream of the day when they will get married and have a child of their own. We play dress up with our mother's clothes and have pretend weddings where Daddy is the groom. Our mothers buy us baby dolls with all of the cute, matching accessories to help us care for our new child. Everything is planned and everything is Perfect.

As an adult, my dreams were the same. I wanted to get married and start a family, have a child of my own. Finally my day came and it was time for me to get married. Everything was planned and everything was perfect. It wasn't long before I wanted to achieve my next dream of having a child. I was excited and nervous all at the same time when I found out I had conceived. This was Perfect...until something went wrong and I learned that I had miscarried. The pain of losing what I wanted so badly seemed unbearable. Everyone said that there was a reason and that I could try again, but all I could think of was, *But I wanted THIS baby.*

My desire to have a child intensified. Two more times I conceived and two more times I experienced the loss. Why was this happening to me? What did I do so wrong that God gave me life and yet it was taken from me? Why

"You made all the delicate, inner parts of my body and knit me together in my mother's womb. Thank you for making me so wonderfully complex!"

PSALM 139: 13-14, NLT

didn't I deserve to have the one thing I so desperately wanted?

Years passed and my dream and desire to have a baby resurfaced. This time, my husband and I planned it … Perfectly.

One beautiful spring day in March, I learned that I was pregnant. I was adamant on doing everything right to ensure that nothing went wrong and I'd hold my baby in my arms nine months later. Thirteen weeks later something bad happened and I thought I was losing my baby. *Dear God, no not again,* is all I could think of. *Please don't do this to me again,* I pleaded.

My body began to take on a new shape and my belly began to grow. I began feeling something that felt like butterfly wings tickling my belly from the inside and I soon learned that those flutters was my baby moving inside of me. I later learned that I was having a girl. I was so excited that I couldn't wait to design her nursery in beautiful shades of lavender and pink, butterflies stenciled on the walls, stuffed animals delicately placed all around, everything so Perfect.

Weeks later I learned that something was wrong with the baby. "There's a fifty percent chance that she has Down Syndrome," they said. "We can do a test to be sure, but we must do it quickly so that you have time to terminate." It was one blow right after the other. I didn't plan this. There goes my Perfect dream, my Perfect baby.

I finally gave birth to my little girl and when I first laid eyes on her beautiful face and looked into her eyes, my outlook changed. This was MY baby, the baby that I longed for, the baby that fought to be here, the baby that God wanted me to have. God did not punish me. I had not done anything wrong. He needed someone to unconditionally love and care for his angel and he thought so highly of Me that he chose Me to be her mother. I had to lose what I wanted most, to see and feel so blessed with the gift I had been given.

"You made all the delicate, inner parts of my body and knit me together in my mother's womb. Thank you for making me so wonderfully complex!" (Psalm 139: 13-14, NLT).

We are all made in God's image.

Adam is missing a rib so that a masterpiece known as a woman could be created. My daughter is God's masterpiece and his most precious gift to me. She is wonderfully made. She was his plan and she is Perfect! And so are you!

Forgiving Daddy, Healing Me

BETTY KOSSICK

As a child, a hard-scrabble existence dogged my steps. My divorced mom struggled at menial jobs to keep us housed and fed. That scenario started for me at age ten. Previously, I had lived for five years in a children's care home. The five years before that, after my babyhood, I often hid in a built-in bookcase to escape my parent's arguments. I stopped my ears, trying not to hear mom's screams, both at him for his drunkenness or because of him battering her.

Hugging my cat proved comforting to me. I told him about the ugliness. I did not have a grandparent or anyone to hold me and say, "I'm sorry," or "I love you." I hated it all. When I saw other girls skipping down the street, holding their daddy's hand, I yearned to be one of them. I did not bellyache to my school chums about my lot. Nor did I reveal the home sadness to my teachers. In those days, family secrets stayed in the closet.

Like many others, during the great American Depression we possessed little, and when daddy guzzled from the bottle, we had less.

Like many others, during the great American Depression we possessed little, and when daddy guzzled from the bottle, we had less. His drinking cronies gave him a sense of camaraderie. Life proved difficult. However, I was not a crybaby about it all. I tried, in my youthful way, to overcome the ugliness surrounding me, in fact, to the point of pretense.

After a severe beating, Mom finally said, "enough" to the miserable life that living with an alcoholic brings and we walked away. Life did not turn into a fairyland existence. In fact, hardship persisted, but the abuse that comes with "life in a bottle" ceased.

Even though I tried to hide it all, I think some of my teachers knew. I still have my second-grade report card on which my teacher wrote, "One of the nicest little girls in the school." Those few words helped me feel special.

At age twelve, I started on my journey with God—hunting for him! Little did I realize that he was the heart-hunter. Six years of searching brought me into a personal knowledge of Jesus as my Lord and Savior, at age eighteen. I discovered that I was created in God's image and he was my Father. I cannot tell you the day or the hour, but along the way, I forgave my earthly father for depriving me of his love, a happy childhood, and my basic needs. If Jesus could forgive those who crucified him, I certainly *must* forgive my dad. I threw away all the passionate feelings of despair that had accumulated in me as a child because of his behavior.

Over the years, I saw him—even visited him in jail—but the encounters were usually stifled, mostly because he reeked of liquor. Because these awkward meetings (some were downright fall-over-drunk times with him and his new wife, another alcoholic), I never told him that I forgave him—that is until my mother died.

The telephone rang across the two-hundred miles that separated us that December afternoon. When I answered it, I heard my father's voice, "Betty Ann, I'm sorry about your mom." He asked a few questions, and I answered. Then he astounded me saying, "I'm sorry that I wasn't the father I should have been."

He had mellowed in his old age and if he smelled of the bottle, I was not exposed to the reek of it—but hearing the words finalized the forgiveness I felt toward him. I told him, "It is okay now, Dad. Mom and I had a tough life. There were times when we did not have anything except canned green beans and black coffee for a meal. We could not buy coal for the furnace. Life hurt. Yet when I accepted Jesus Christ as Lord of my life, I asked Jesus to forgive me of my sins and along the way, I also forgave you."
He thanked me. Four months later he, too, died.

Domestic abuse is devilish. However, our Creator offers us the ability to forgive, be forgiven, and healing comes.

"…bearing with one another, and forgiving one another…even as Christ forgave you, so you must also do" (Colossians 3:13, NKJV).

That
Newspaper
on the
Floor!

ANA BOUDET FORMAN

*W*hy is it so hard for my husband to put the newspaper in the magazine basket next to his chair after he's finished reading it, instead of leaving it all over the floor?

It is like any typical afternoon driving my girls home from school. I'm trying to concentrate on the traffic, but my mind is going a mile a minute as I think about the errands I need to run before I go home. My older daughter needs fabric paint to decorate a T-shirt. It is my Kindergartener's turn to bring the snack. Oh, gosh…what's a healthy snack? Those young moms are always so clever with their homemade granola bars decorated with raisin smiley faces. I'm too old to have a five-year-old! What am I cooking tonight? Could my husband pick up dinner?

The cell phone rings and snaps me back out of my mental tirade. It's my husband who calmly informs me that after his routine blood work that morning his doctor called and told him he didn't like the numbers of his platelet count. He wants my husband to have another blood test immediately. Okay, I say, and wonder out loud what it all means. My husband shrugs off my question by telling me the doctor is just being overly cautious. We hang up, with my husband promising to be home soon with dinner. But I'm left with a

By 8 o'clock that evening we are at the hospital on the oncology floor waiting for more blood work results.

71

knot in the pit of my stomach. This isn't a big deal, is it?

By 8 o'clock that evening we are at the hospital on the oncology floor waiting for more blood work results. As it has turned out, my husband's platelet counts are so low the second time around that his doctor wants him admitted to the hospital. I'm somewhere between numb and dazed as I hear words like leukemia and bone marrow biopsy. It will take several days for any conclusive diagnosis, so we just have to wait.

Each night during the time my husband was in the hospital, I tried to keep a normal routine. As I got ready for bed, I checked in on my five-year-old and adjusted her favorite teddy bear to fit cozily under her arm. I poked my head into my teenager's room and told her to get off the phone and go to sleep! I'd always give the family room a quick look and pick up any wayward pair of shoes and such. Ordinarily, I'd dig out the remote from a seat cushion and routinely collect and put away the newspaper that my husband would have left on the floor. But on those nights the newspaper was already folded in the magazine basket. I had put it there earlier because I had not had time to read it, and of course, my husband wasn't home to read it either. I broke down in tears.

That night I knelt on my bedroom floor and prayed. My prayer wasn't particularly eloquent. I just prayed that God would bring my husband home so he would be able to toss that newspaper

That night I prayed that God would bring my husband home so he would be able to toss that newspaper on the floor again.

on the floor. A couple of days later, we received the results of the biopsy. It was not leukemia. His condition was brought on by medication and was easily treated.

The evening my husband came home from the hospital the house was filled with joyful commotion and family. Late that night, the house finally quiet, I followed my usual bedtime routine. I tidied up the sofa cushions, folded the afghan, and noticed the newspaper strewn on the floor next to my husband's chair. As I picked it up and placed it in the basket, my eyes swelled with tears. I had never been so happy to pick up a newspaper in my entire life.

Years have passed since that incident. I have picked up that newspaper many a night. I'm not going to pretend I'm giddy about having to do it every time, but has my attitude changed! I know it is a privilege to have people to love and care for… and to be loved and cared for in return. I'll never forget when there was no need to pick up that newspaper, and I thank God each night as I fold that paper and put it neatly back in the basket.

Sweet Words

PATTY KNITTEL

*M*y mother-in-law came to live with us for her last ten months of her life. She had chronic myeloid leukemia and had fought it for nine years.

I knew all along this was the right thing to do when the time came. But, I have to admit, I was apprehensive about having her with us all the time. I always felt I had disappointed her as a daughter-in-law because she had always looked forward to someone who liked feminine things, like cooking and sewing. Her tastes in decoration hadn't fit my taste, either, so when she asked us what we wanted before she sold everything, I only picked the grandfather clock, and her Franciscan dishes.

She moved up to Oregon from California and settled in. It was a huge move for her and yet she handled it so well. She had to have known she didn't have long to live, thus resigning herself to the move. The grandfather clock and dishware were among the few belongings she brought with her.

I was working part-time so it was nice to have her there to greet the kids when they came home from school. It was also great when she volunteered to cook supper sometimes. For the most part, though, she stayed to herself in her basement room complete with her own refrigerator and TV.

"Dear friends, since God so loved us, we also ought to love one another"

1 John 4:11, NIV.

It actually came to the point that I was trying to

get her to join us when we watched TV, when we had company, or when we went out to a movie. But, she didn't want to intrude. I really felt bad about it. My husband tried to assure me she could be stubborn and not to take it personally.

As the months passed, her strength began to go down and she needed blood transfusions one or two times a week for energy. Oh, how she hated those. She was so frail, but determined to keep fighting the disease. The medication was no longer effective. She was dying, but we didn't talk about it.

Finally, the doctor suggested hospice. She surprisingly agreed. She knew it would help us out, too, as we were taking turns helping her at night. A week into their care, the visiting nurse sat down with her to talk about the transfusions. She told

A few nights later, I was tucking her into bed. I told her goodnight, and she said in a frail voice, "Goodnight, sweet thing."

mother she didn't have to have any more unless she wanted them. It was like giving her permission to let go. She stopped them that week.

A hospital bed was put in the living room. She was going downhill fast. She had a terrible fall one night as she tried to get to the bathroom without calling us to help.

A few nights later, I was tucking her into bed. I told her goodnight, and she said in a frail voice, "Goodnight, sweet thing." I was glad it was dark because the tears welled up in my eyes. I kissed her and went to my room. Those were her last words to me.

She died the next day. She left me with the gift of knowing she loved me. I will always cherish that. I hope I let my family know each day that I love them, not waiting for tragedy to wake me to the opportunity.

"Like apples of gold in settings of silver

Is a word spoken in right circumstances" (Proverbs 25:11, NASB).

Hearing by God's Grace

KIMBERLY QUINNIE

Kimberly! Kimberly!" called my mother. "I love you, too!" I replied from another room in the house. The entire house erupted with laughter as my brothers held their sides and rolled on the floor. To my dismay, I had done it... again. Would it ever get better? Would I ever be able to understand the words people expressed when speaking to me at a distance? Would I always need to see a person's mouth when they spoke to me in order to understand them?

Being hearing impaired has never been easy. Sometimes, I'd try to shield myself from the taunts and cruelty of other children by making them laugh or being the quietest in the group because of the awkwardness of the hearing aids I wore. I obtained my first pair in 1985 when it wasn't really popular to be that kind of different. My siblings and mother helped me adjust to them by playing games and practicing "distance hearing" with me and teaching me to have self-confidence. They taught me to not be afraid to "try" to hear the things in my environment; encouraging me to be the best in everything that I attempted in life. The fact that everybody has something that is unique about them instilled in me a desire to help others that struggle with the same disability. My family told me that one day I would be a very influential person in the field of hearing impaired.

"...Nothing in all creation will ever be able to separate us from the love of God..."
ROMANS 8:39, NLT.

As a child growing up in the '80s, I found it difficult to separate my personality from my disability. I was "the kid with the hearing aids" and it seemed as though my aids announced my presence everywhere I went. Children would stare and adults would whisper. It was so uncomfortable that I began to feel as though I was some sort of alien from outer space at times. It was *not* easy. My siblings encouraged me to explain to others that I was hearing impaired and that hearing aids helped me to hear clearer. *I* simply wanted to live a life that didn't point to my ears so much.

I begged my mother to buy every new hearing aid that was invented in a smaller version than the one that I currently had. As I grew into my teenage years, I noticed that the difficulties that I experienced in school as a hearing impaired individual began to define my life. Every school I attended was characterized by teachers that either helped or hurt me because of my disability. In college, some of my instructors created difficulties pertaining to my lack of ability to hearing things clearly. Every experience made me stronger in the face of adversity even when it hurt the very core of my being. My family always encouraged me to move forward because "God has a special work for you to do for the deaf and hard of hearing" and that I should use my disability for the advancement of others rather than allow it to be a hindrance for myself.

Because of the struggles I faced, the Lord placed

I simply wanted to live a life that didn't point to my ears so much.

within me a desire to help others with hearing disabilities. I attended a small university and majored in Deaf Education. This prepared me to face the world armed with the mentality that deaf and hard of hearing people can be successful, too! I created a deaf ministry; teaching groups of people to use sign language. I started sign language choirs in various locations as a ministry to the deaf. Many lives were touched and the effects of my ministry are still felt in different parts of the world today. Since graduating from college, my profession has exposed me to undreamable advantages! I became a deaf advocate; teaching parents of hearing impaired children how to communicate with their child. I also teach children to succeed academically despite their disability.

My ministry has touched the world in a very unique way; allowing my musical sign language ministry to be a blessing wherever I go. My life's motto has become: NOTHING can separate us from God's love, not even deafness!

I Love You Just the Way You Are!

DAWN BROWN

One day my three-year-old son did something and I yelled at him. A few minutes later, as I realized I had completely over-reacted, I went back to him and told him Mommy was wrong for yelling and asked him for forgiveness. He took his little hands and cupped my face and replied, "That's okay, Mommy. I forgive you." And then he added sweetly, "I love you just the way you are!"

My heart melted! I had never heard him say that last part before, and the words permeated my heart, as they do even now, as I replay them again. They were the loving words a mom, who often feels like a failure, needed to hear.

Interestingly, ever since, I've come to believe that is exactly what God says about his love toward me, "I love you just the way you are. It doesn't matter what you've done, who you have hurt, or how badly the mess you've made of your life. I love you just the way you are!" In Romans 5, Paul writes of God's love for us while we were still in sin. You see, even before we realize our wrong, even before we come to God for forgiveness, he had already demonstrated his great love for us by dying on the cross for our sins. The chapter goes on to say we were "enemies of God" and yet his love was

"But God showed his great love for us by sending Christ to die for us while we were still sinners" ROMANS 5:8, NLT.

83

so great, so unconditional, so unchanging that even before you and I wanted anything to do with him, he loved us. That means God's love is not dependent on our goodness. He doesn't love us more because we're good, and love us less because we're bad. His love is the kind of love that says in word and action, "I love you just the way you are!"

Once we understand that God's love for us is unconditional and non-changing, we ought to be like my toddler son, and graciously dispense that same kind of love to others. Whether we feel wronged by our spouse or a friend, exasperated by our kids, or perhaps a boss who is demanding, unreasonable, maybe even condescending – understanding God's great, unconditional love should compel us to love others, no matter how undeserving they may seem! Remember, they, too, were created in the image of God, and have intrinsic worth in his sight. The relationship may be strained, and we may not like everything about that person, but loving others like we are loved by God means we are quick to forgive and willing to work to restore the brokenness in every relationship.

Of course, there are still days when my son still tries my patience (as kids sometimes do) but now, I rest in God's unfailing love, and trust that his presence is with me and strengthening me with exactly what I need to rightly represent him and his amazing love. Loving our children and others just the way they are, helps them understand that no matter what they say or do, God loves them just the way they are. If I sow that seed into their tender hearts, I trust that it will reap in them a genuine love for their Savior, too.

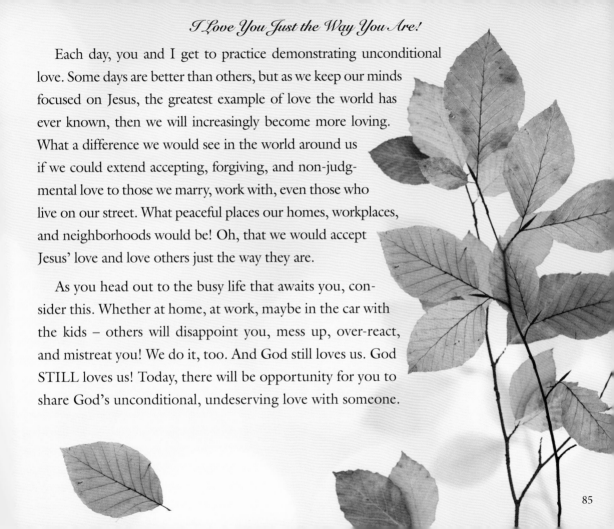

I Love You Just the Way You Are!

Each day, you and I get to practice demonstrating unconditional love. Some days are better than others, but as we keep our minds focused on Jesus, the greatest example of love the world has ever known, then we will increasingly become more loving. What a difference we would see in the world around us if we could extend accepting, forgiving, and non-judgmental love to those we marry, work with, even those who live on our street. What peaceful places our homes, workplaces, and neighborhoods would be! Oh, that we would accept Jesus' love and love others just the way they are.

As you head out to the busy life that awaits you, consider this. Whether at home, at work, maybe in the car with the kids – others will disappoint you, mess up, over-react, and mistreat you! We do it, too. And God still loves us. God STILL loves us! Today, there will be opportunity for you to share God's unconditional, undeserving love with someone.

A Turn Around

ARLENE SALIBA

I'm sorry to bother you. I know you are here to do paper work, but the wife of one of our patients wants to talk to you," the clinic nurse said. The day was reserved for reviewing lab results and notifying patients of those results. Spouses usually accompany the patient. If this woman had come by herself, there must be a real problem.

The nurse ushered in a distressed woman, who told me her husband was drinking six to eight beers every day, falling because of seizures, and was not contributing to the home chores nor expenses. She was doing everything in the house including caring for their child with special needs and working outside the home. She didn't like seeing him have seizures and didn't understand why he was having them even if he had not missed his medications. He was not abusive verbally or physically. He just didn't DO anything but sit around and drink. She was tired and fed up but also worried about her husband. She asked for advice … or the name of a lawyer I could recommend.

"Teach me, O Lord, the way of Your statutes, and I shall keep it to the end. Give me understanding and I shall keep Your law; indeed, I shall observe it with my whole heart" PSALM 119: 33-34, NKJV.

"Do you love him?" I asked. Through sobs and tears she nodded her head. A lawyer's name was not on my list that day. We talked about her role as a wife and mother.

I asked her to be the best wife she could possibly be no matter what her husband did and let the chips fall where they will. She was reminded to also care for herself. She did not have to be super woman and do everything.

A few days later, she was back with her husband who now had an appointment. The tension in the room was palpable. She sat in a corner with her arms folded. Weary eyes of steel stared at the wall. He was downcast, eyes slightly bloodshot and obviously nervous. He looked like a broken man—almost like a child who had been scolded and didn't know where to hide. He said, "This is a wake-up call and I don't know what to do. She handed me divorce papers yesterday. I don't want this. Please help me."

After making sure that he was physically intact, my advice to them was: "Take your medicines like you should. Eat nutritious food, not empty calories. Stop buying beer. Be active. Go for a walk together . . . and hold hands. Reaffirm one another during this walk. This is not a time to argue or discuss issues. Enjoy each other's company. Go to church together. Pray together. Lastly, forgive one another."

"That's it?" he said. "I can do that. I'll eat whatever she puts in front of me. We live near the lake; we can walk there. I just don't

She was tired and fed up but also worried about her husband. She asked for advice … or the name of a lawyer I could recommend.

know if she will hold my hand after all that I have done. I used to go to church with her until . . ." He looked nervously at her. She threw daggers at him with her eyes. He looked away then back at her hopefully. She smiled weakly and said "We can give it a try. I really don't want a divorce, but I'm not going to put up with you the way you were."

In a month they were back. From outside the examining room I could hear them talking and giggling like high school sweethearts. "This is the man I married!" she said. Her husband had not had any beer since leaving the clinic the month before. He also had not had any seizures. They were doing everything I suggested and more. He was working in the yard on projects that had been neglected. Their daughter was much happier also. The divorce papers had been burned. They were working on a weight loss program together and planning a short vacation. They were thankful for a new direction in their lives. So was I.

God Says, "I Love You"

JOANNE CORTES

The other day I was busy working and my son asked for something to eat, so I gave him a snack. Five minutes later he was thirsty. A few minutes after, "Mom, can I watch something, please?"

"Honey, I am trying to work here, go play." At that moment I began to get a little stressed.

If you haven't yet done so, make a commitment to begin your day communicating with God and taking time to love your family and friends. When you do this, it will result in inner peace, greater happiness, better relationships, stronger faith, and true satisfaction for you and your loved ones. God will be happy, too.

"Mom, I'm hungry again,"

"Mom, can you fix this toy?"

"Mom, play with me."

By now I was more concerned about my work getting done than helping my child. I was overwhelmed by so many requests that I snapped at him, "Leave me alone! Can't you see I'm working? Go to your play room."

Before he went sadly to his play room, he says "I love you, Mom."

Hold on, did I hear right? Did my son just say that he loved me after the way I've been treating him? This made me feel really bad, like the worst mom ever. *What did I just do? He is my son. What is wrong with me? Nothing is more important than him!*

Have you felt this way before? Guilty of ignoring your child and snapping at him just because he asked? Maybe you don't have a child, but you may have treated someone unfairly because you were too busy. At times we get caught up in all of life's demanding activities, we are overwhelmed and stressed, causing us to mistreat and hurt people, especially those closest to us. We tell them to leave us alone, we don't have time, we don't call back, we don't spend time together, or sit around the table for dinner—we are just too busy. We isolate ourselves in our "to do list" in this harsh world only to later realize that we are missing life's most valuable blessings, awesome quality time with our family and great relationships with our friends, neighbors, and colleagues.

The saddest thing is that at times I act this way with God. Just like my son wanted to spend time with me, God is next to me wanting to spend time together. He wants to share special moments and bless me with his presence, but I push him away. And he still says: "I Love You!" And he says those same words to you. These words are all we need to hear to break us and to help us realize he loves us. Though at times he may not be on our priority list, he patiently waits for us to say, "I love you,

"But God is so rich in mercy, and he loved us so much"

EPHESIANS 2:4, NLT.

too! Let's spend some time together."

Life is too short to not spend time with the One person who loves us more than anyone or anything.

Take time today to talk with God. Throughout the day, tell him what you are going through. He sees and knows everything, yet he wants to hear it from you. He wants you to acknowledge his presence. He wants to bless you and love you more than you could ever imagine! He wants you to know that he is available 24/7 for you!

If you haven't yet done so, make a commitment to begin your day communicating with God and taking time to love your family and friends. When you do this, it will result in inner peace, greater happiness, better relationships, stronger faith, and true satisfaction for you and your loved ones. God will be happy, too.

And of course, when you are fulfilled and blessed, success in your work, inside and outside the home, will follow.

Heaven's Stand-in

COLLENE KELLY

Although the late summer sun shone brightly, it did not warm my husband's heart. "I don't know if I want to stay in the ministry. Nothing seems to change, and who really cares about whether the church fails or not? I'm still young. I can go back to school and do something different," he said.

It wasn't the first time he had verbalized these thoughts. In fact, over the previous several weeks, his courage for the incessant calling of ministry had been as low as the attendance at prayer meeting. And although I cared about my spouse, I couldn't relate to his restlessness.

Nodding and smiling at the members the next day, I settled, with our toddler, into a pew and prepared for an hour of church. Since I had heard the same sermon just seven days earlier at another of our churches, I knew I could coast through this week, the story of Elijah running from Jezebel still quite fresh in memory. But instead I began to wonder about the "Elijah" in my life. How could the shepherd of the flock feel so much like getting away from the sheepfold? Why couldn't he lie down in green pastures and drink from still water himself?

Sometimes something miraculous happens during a sermon. Surely that is part of the reason we are admonished not to forsake the assembling of ourselves together, and all the more so as Jesus' return nears (see Hebrews

"I don't know if I want to stay in the ministry."

10:25). Sometimes the Spirit plucks an arrow from the quiver of the Word and shoots it directly to the heart.

As my disgruntled thoughts jumbled about, I kept one ear to the sermon and pondered Elijah's story: "…while he himself went a day's journey into the desert. He came to a broom tree, sat down under it and prayed that he might die. 'I have had enough, Lord,' he said. 'Take my life; I am no better than my ancestors.' Then he lay down under the tree and fell asleep. All at once an angel touched him and said, 'Get up and eat.' He looked around, and there by his head was a cake of bread baked over hot coals, and a jar of water. He ate and drank and then lay down again" (1 Kings 19:4-6, NIV).

And then it was that the Great Shepherd spoke to me: "When my servant ran away, I sent an angel to feed and care for him. What are you doing to care for your Elijah?" Chastened and chagrined, I repented of my hard heart, and accepted anew the ministry of encouragement. Challenges come and go. Opportunities and requests to serve are unending, but my greatest ministry potential is to care for my husband.

Every man who stands for Jesus faces moments when he feels alone. Satan whispers discouraging sentiments to weaken his faith, occasionally even through trusted friends or family. Plans will fail, and days are long. When labor is exhausting, friends misunderstand, and life seems only uphill, then it is that we can care as the angel did for Elijah.

We can listen, love, and encourage, give the gift of understanding, feel his pain, and bring him to Jesus in prayer. Elijah had no wife, and God sent him a heavenly messenger. Your husband has you—heaven's angel for the Elijah in your life.

And, as the continuation of Elijah's story whispers, we can remember that sometimes he needs time, as well as rest and refreshment, in order to regain his energy and courage so he can get back to the fray. "The angel of the Lord came back a second time and touched him and said, 'Get up and eat, for the journey is too much for you.' So he got up and ate and drank. Strengthened by that food, he traveled forty days and forty nights until he reached Horeb, the mountain of God. There he went into a cave and spent the night." The next morning, the Lord instructed him, "Go out and stand on the mountain in the presence of the Lord, for the Lord is about to pass by" (see 1 Kings 19:7-9, 11, NIV).

Then in quick succession came a mountain shattering wind, an earthquake, and a fire, followed by a still, small voice that would remind him that although in his discouragement, Elijah had decided that he alone was left to stand for God, there were still 7,000 faithful men in Israel. In this, Elijah found comfort, hope, and rejuvenation.

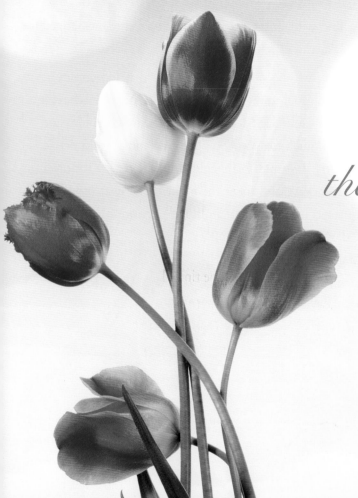

Trust the Expert

CARLA BAKER

*O*n a busy Sunday afternoon, I had just finished cleaning the kitchen after a late lunch. As I mentally planned my chores for the rest of the day, the back door burst open and in bounded my 12-year-old son, Brandon.

"Mom!" he said in a strange voice. When I turned to look at him, I first noticed that his face registered a look of alarm. Then I quickly saw the reason for his distress: blood was dripping from his hand and arm.

Though my instinctive reaction to the sight of blood is to panic and look away, I knew I had to stay calm and find out the nature of the injury. As I put his hand under the faucet to wash off the blood and get a look at the damage, I saw that the skin appeared to be torn away from the tip of his right index finger, leaving the bone exposed and jagged-looking.

As we drove home, I asked why he had watched while the surgeon worked on his hand. It had been too gory for me. Brandon's reply astonished me: "I was afraid the doctor would decide to cut off my whole finger, and I wasn't going to let him."

With a quivering voice, Brandon gave me a sketchy description of what had happened. He had been riding his bicycle in the neighborhood when the chain came off the gears. Without stopping to get off the bike, he bent over to guide the chain back onto the gears as the wheels were turning. His right index finger got caught between the chain and gears, and the tip of the finger was mashed.

As calmly as I could, I wrapped a kitchen towel around his hand, and we headed to the hospital emergency room. When we were ushered into the examination cubicle, I was relieved to learn that the doctor examining Brandon's finger was a surgeon. He said that the bone was splintered and would not heal, so the splintered portion, just a few millimeters, had to be clipped off. He reassured us that the skin would soon grow back over the tip and Brandon would have full use of the finger again, although it would be quite sensitive for awhile.

Brandon had always been a squeamish kid who couldn't stand the sight of blood, but I noticed that as the surgeon clipped away the splintered bone and sutured the skin back together, Brandon watched intently during the entire process. As we drove home, I asked why he had watched while the surgeon worked on his hand. It had been too gory for me. Brandon's reply astonished me: "I was afraid the doctor would decide to cut off my whole finger, and I wasn't going to let him."

I had to hide a rueful smile at the unfounded fears of a child—fears that only increased his agony during his emergency room experience. He would have had a much easier time had he trusted the person in charge, who was trained and knew exactly what to do.

Since that day I have reflected on the times that I, too, fail to experience peace of mind because I don't trust the One who has the answers to all my problems and is more than willing to help me.

The apostle Paul tells us in Philippians 4:6-7 how to experience peace of mind in even the most trying circumstances: *"Do not be anxious about anything, but in every situation, by prayer and petition, with thanksgiving, present your requests to God. And the peace of God, which transcends all understanding, will guard your hearts and your minds in Christ Jesus"* (NIV).

How reassuring to know that our heavenly Father not only has the answers to all our questions and problems, but he always wants the very best for his children.

He must shake his head in amazement when we fail to take advantage of the peace that comes from trusting in his tender care.

Lord, please give me faith to trust you more.

Too Busy to Rest

CHERYL MOSELEY

*S*canning quickly through her planner, Sarah knew she had another busy week ahead. Every day was full of activities and this week she had agreed to work overtime. Apart from going to work and taking the children to their various after-school programs, Sarah needed to go to the gym, attend meetings, arrange a car service, do the grocery shopping and housework, and continue with her online Spanish course. Even for Sarah it looked like a hectic week.

In fact, most weeks were the same. Life was so busy that Sarah had little time for relaxation and leisure. She often spent half the night catching up on chores and was always up early the next day after only a few hours sleep. Sarah was a young, working mom with lots of energy; she enjoyed her busy lifestyle, but lately she was beginning to feel tired. She tried to shake off the feeling and carry on, telling herself how important her tasks were.

On Monday morning after dropping the children at school, Sarah rushed to the gym for a half-hour exercise class. After that it

"Do not be anxious about anything, but in every situation, by prayer and petition, with thanksgiving, present your requests to God. And the peace of God, which transcends all understanding, will guard your hearts and your minds in Christ Jesus" NIV.

was on to work. Her boss was taking assessments of his staff that afternoon, so everyone in the office was under pressure to perform. One thing after another seemed to go wrong that morning and by lunch time Sarah felt extremely stressed and anxious. There was still so much to do she didn't have time for a break, so she worked through lunch. Often Sarah would wish she could just sit down and do nothing for five minutes, but it never happened!

Around five o'clock Sarah put the finishing touches to an important presentation for a client, which needed to be mailed out that day. As she was rushing downstairs to the mail room she suddenly felt faint and the room began to spin. Then everything went black. She woke feeling pain in her right leg. Looking around she realized she was in the hospital, her leg in plaster. She had blacked out on the stairs and taken a fall. The doctor stood by her bed.

"Come with me by yourselves to a quiet place and get some rest"

MARK 6:31, NIV.

"You had a nasty fall" he told her. "It's going to take many weeks and lots of rest for your leg to heal."

Great! How could she afford to rest? There was so much to do. At first Sarah felt this was a nightmare situation. How would everything get done? Who would take the kids to school? What would happen to her job? Thoughts like this crowded her mind until she remembered something her mother taught her as a child. It was a verse from the Bible: *"Come to me all you who are weary and burdened, and I will give you rest. Take my yoke upon you and learn from me for I am gentle and humble in heart, and you will find rest for your souls"* (*Matthew 11:28-29, NIV*).

It was then she realized that God was using these circumstances to enable her to get the rest she so desired and needed; rest her body had been crying out for.

Sarah's leg healed and she returned to work. Today she lives a much more balanced lifestyle. She makes time to rest every day – a walk in the park, reading a good book, or maybe just closing her eyes and putting her feet up. She even makes sure she gets a good night's sleep, too. Life has changed a lot for Sarah, but the funny thing is, she says she achieves so much more now than she ever did before!

My Friend's Baditude

CODI JAHN

*A*ttitude is everything. We've all heard it. But can you really control your attitude in all circumstances? A friend of mine told a story years ago about attitude that I've never forgotten. This friend was diagnosed with an aggressive form of cancer that would require intense therapy if he was going to have any shot at all of beating it. He and his wife both quit their jobs and relocated cross country to be near the treatment facility. The treatments were exhausting and incredibly painful.

One day, not unlike all the others during his treatment, my friend was riding the elevator up to the cancer treatment floor. Another gentleman stepped on and they began riding up together. "Beautiful day outside, isn't it?" commented the passenger, enthusiastically. My friend glanced up at him and his cheery demeanor. He hadn't really noticed the weather; he was a little preoccupied trying to beat cancer! But then what would this guy know of that?

In his world, thought my friend, *there's nothing more important to focus your energy on than the weather. He has no idea what it is like to look*

"Do not be anxious about anything, but in every situation, by prayer and petition, with thanksgiving, present your requests to God. And the peace of God, which transcends all understanding, will guard your hearts and your minds in Christ Jesus" NIV.

death in the face every day and try to find the strength to struggle on. They continued riding up, both eventually stopping at the cancer floor.

My friend waited patiently to sign in behind Mr. Optimistic. After all, anyone going through what he was going through could use a visitor like him. As he removed his jacket and hat, my friend saw his hairless head and realized he was no visitor; he, too, was there for the fight of his life. He was a fellow cancer patient, no different than my friend, yet he had chosen to see beauty despite all the ugliness he was up against.

My friend never saw him again. They never rode the elevator up together after that, but he learned an important lesson that day that he later shared with me. No matter what your circumstance, or what battles you're fighting, you control your attitude. Life may dictate your surroundings and those around you may control your decisions, but only you determine your attitude.

I was surprised to hear this story from my friend, someone I had always considered to personify optimism. Yet even he was susceptible to life's pressures. He seemed embarrassed as he shared his experience, but he had learned a valuable lesson about his attitude.

"...always seek after that which is good for one another and for all people. Rejoice always; pray without ceasing; in everything give thanks; for this is God's will for you in Christ Jesus"

1 Thess. 5:15, 18 NASB.

I have never battled cancer or fought for my life. To be honest, things have been pretty easy. Still, each day presents new obstacles. As a newly transitioned stay-at-home mom, I've seen more lately than usual. During one of my son's notorious temper tantrums, I began sinking into despair, remembering the "good times" I'd had at my fulfilling job and all the adult interaction it entailed (something I get very little of now). I felt sorry for myself and wondered why I had ever wanted to do this in the first place.

Just then I thought of my friend and his experience with a stranger on an elevator. I, too, was choosing my own attitude. Staying home with my son had been a dream of mine for years, so was I going to let a tantrum or two really impair my attitude? How would that help my son's struggling attitude?

Instead of feeling sorry for myself, I began to feel thankful for the opportunity before me; being able to influence and touch my children's lives in a way I had always wished to . . . and having enough time to do it.

Fear Not the Cat

JEAN THOMASON ("MISS PATTYCAKE")

*I*t was nearly noon and the trip to the grocery store had taken longer than I wanted. All three of us were cranky. Grocery shopping takes more energy than I ever think it will. And, it really wears out the children! I finally checked out, wrestled them into the car, and drove toward home.

"Mommy, I'm hungry. I'm thirsty, too. How long till we get home? Will it rain today? What color is the moon? Do fish have teeth? Christopher won't be quiet!"

Even getting out of the car is a chore! My ten-month-old son was fussing loudly and was heavy on my right arm in the car carrier while my other arm was loaded with grocery bags. "Go straight into the house please," I instructed twenty-seven-month-old Marilyn, who slowly walked up the front porch stairs in front of me. I felt like a shepherd, herding her toward the door. Time for lunch and naps. "Please hurry! Mommy is *tired*."

"Mommy, I'm hungry. I'm thirsty, too. How long till we get home? Will it rain today? What color is the moon? Do fish have teeth? Christopher won't be quiet!"

Suddenly she stopped, screamed, and ran to the other end of our wide front porch. There was a kitty near our front door. Not our kitty – a strange kitty – a big, hairy cat. Marilyn was terrified! Speaking soothing words to Marilyn, I walked calmly past the cat to the door. It looked at me. I looked at it. It didn't move. I unlocked the front door, being careful not to drop bags or baby. "Come on sweetie, mommy sees the cat," I urged. "The cat won't get you." I shooed the cat. It lazily walked a few feet from the door. Marilyn was not moving. "Honey, I won't let the cat hurt you."

"The cat, the cat!" she wailed. Holding the door open, I said, "The kitty will not hurt you. Just please run on into the house."

"No. No! It's a *big* cat!" she whined. Frustrated, I said, "Marilyn, look at me. Don't look at the cat. Walk to *me* and come into the house."

She didn't move. (My arms are aching now).

"Please honey – don't look at the cat," I said. "I will not let the cat hurt you. Look at me." I was begging…rather *loudly* now – the baby was crying and I was on the brink…. "Sweetie! If that cat comes anywhere near you, I will KICK it away!"

Finally! After much coaxing she took a tentative step, looked at me, then the cat, then me, the cat, me, cat, and *ran* past me into the house. Whew! I turned to the cat, stomped my foot and said, "Scat!" The strange cat flew off our porch, never to return.

Later, I pondered that episode, and had an "AHA" moment. How like our Father to show me something profound in a typical "mothering" day. From his perspective, I am that scared little girl – afraid of the "cats" in my life. The Father is urging me, "Look at *Me* – not the cats. Keep your eyes on me – I will not let the 'cats' hurt you. Walk the way

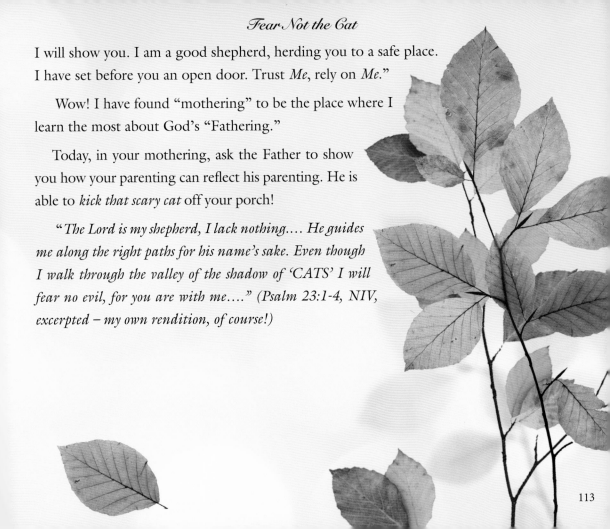

I will show you. I am a good shepherd, herding you to a safe place. I have set before you an open door. Trust *Me*, rely on *Me*."

Wow! I have found "mothering" to be the place where I learn the most about God's "Fathering."

Today, in your mothering, ask the Father to show you how your parenting can reflect his parenting. He is able to *kick that scary cat* off your porch!

"The Lord is my shepherd, I lack nothing…. He guides me along the right paths for his name's sake. Even though I walk through the valley of the shadow of 'CATS' I will fear no evil, for you are with me…." (Psalm 23:1-4, NIV, excerpted – my own rendition, of course!)

Just a Routine Test

PATRICIA BODI

*T*he postcard came from the doctor's office reminding me it was time for the annual checkup. It was in January and, unfortunately, I was knee-deep in taxes. You see — I'm an accountant-tax-preparer. I just didn't have time for doctor's visits. So I neglected to call for an appointment.

Once the filing period was over and I had returned from a week's vacation with my mother in Florida, I went in to see the physician on April 30. About ten days later I received a phone call at my home from my doctor's office informing me that I had abnormal cells and they had made an appointment with a specialist for a biopsy.

After I had allowed this information to soak in and I had talked privately with the Lord about it, I realized I needed to talk further about it. But who would I call? Should I call a family member? After all, I had a mother and four sisters living in the area. Should I call a classmate from academy days or college? Should I call one of my children? No, I called a good friend from church, Betty.

If you knew Betty, you would have no problem hearing her say, "We'll have lunch after the biopsy." And we did. Afterwards I went in to work.

First, Betty and I just talked. Then she prayed a beautiful prayer with me over the telephone as she often does with church friends.

Finally, Betty insisted on going with me to the physician's office the next week. I've been single for many years and not used to being accompanied to the doctor's office. However, Betty was so persuasive that I easily acquiesced. If you knew Betty, you would have no problem hearing her say, "We'll have lunch after the biopsy." And we did. Afterwards I went in to work.

And then I waited and waited for the verdict. Now if you have ever had a biopsy, you know it takes FOREVER to learn the results! After the results—"inconclusive"—I returned to the doctor's office. Then I was instructed to use a topical application for about a month. During this time my father was in hospice on his deathbed, so I cancelled my return visit. After my dad's funeral, I returned to the doctor's office for the next test.

One week later, my doctor's office called me at work to arrange for laser surgery. Unfortunately, the treatment had made no difference.

The surgery took place at the local hospital where I had been a volunteer chaplain assistant for ten years. One month later, I was happy to learn the lab results showed it was pre-cancerous and "the margins are clear."

"Inasmuch as ye have done it unto one of the least of these my brethren, ye have done it unto me"

MATTHEW 25:40, KJV.

Praise the Lord!

When I was most in need of emotional

and spiritual support, Betty was there to provide nurturing to a church sister. Now, isn't that what God talks about in Matthew 25:40? *"Inasmuch as ye have done it unto one of the least of these my brethren, ye have done it unto me"* (KJV).

It's been suggested that how we treat others is literally how we're treating our Savior. If we could always remember him, we would see each other through his eyes. We'd be more forgiving, more compassionate and more giving. We'd reach out to others, lift, build and bless, for in doing so, we know we're doing what God expects of his church. Furthermore, we would be following the example of my good friend, Betty.

"Therefore encourage one another and build each other up, just as in fact you are doing" (1 Thessalonians 5:11, NIV).

Angels
All Around Us!

JUDITH NEWTON

My husband and I were on a vacation in Oahu, Hawaii. It was our anniversary and we were having a fantastic time. Now before I go further, I have to tell you how awesome our God is. Before I left, one of my best friends came to me and told me that she felt the Lord was telling her to seriously pray for me while I was gone. She felt that I would be in some kind of danger. I just tucked her words in the back of my mind.

So we were on this beautiful island enjoying ourselves. We rented a car to take a tour of the island. At the car rental place the attendant warned us about the "south side" of the island. He said the currents were bad there, and sometimes rogue waves were known to carry people out to sea and they drowned. We both thanked him and drove away. I wasn't concerned much. I couldn't swim and I had no intention of getting that close to the ocean. When I was young I had almost drowned in a lake and I have been somewhat fearful of being in the water since then.

"Don't forget to show hospitality to strangers, for some who have done this have entertained angels without realizing it!"

HEBREWS 13:2, NLT.

We were driving along admiring the cobalt blue skies, the lush green forests, and majestic vistas. We both felt like it was just a little bit of heaven. When we arrived at the south side, the view was absolutely spectacular, and we could see why people would want to walk the beach.

We decided to get out of the car and walk on the beach, back far enough we felt we were safe from any rogue wave. We walked along like a newly married couple, holding hands (even after thirty-two years of marriage, we still hold hands).

I wasn't concerned at all. I was sure we were far enough from the edge of the ocean to be safe. But suddenly, without any warning, a rogue wave dashed against the beach and immediately pulled us out to sea! I found myself being drawn down under the thrashing waves. I remember thinking, *I am going to die*. In my heart I cried out to the Lord.

I was being tumbled over and over against the coral reef there. I was being pushed deeper and deeper into the depths of the ocean, and being buffeted by the pounding waves. I could feel the pull of the current on my body. I was being pummeled by the waves. I was choking on the sea water and everything seemed hopeless.

Suddenly I had the sensation of being gently plucked out of the water. The next thing I knew I was sitting on a log at the edge of the beach. People were all around me. They had seen we were in serious trouble and ran to see if they could help. Strangely, I was filled with a profound feeling of peace and calmness. My

Without any warning, a rogue wave dashed against the beach and immediately pulled us out to sea! I found myself being drawn down under the thrashing waves. I remember thinking, I am going to die.

husband, who can swim well, was sitting on the beach close to me looking like a drowned cat.

I looked at my legs and feet and realized I had deep cuts all over them from the coral. I could tell one big toe was broken. My hands had cuts all over them as I had tried frantically to grab hold of something to help me. My right arm was sprained and I was bruised all over. Yet, here I sat, perfectly calm and relaxed.

I should have been absolutely beside myself with fear and shock. But I wasn't! You see I KNEW that the Lord had an angel scoop me up out of the water and put me on that log. There was no other explanation for what happened.

Do angels exist? Oh yes, they certainly do.

As we travel through this world we are under the constant care and protection of heavenly angels. We all have a guardian angel that walks with us and guards us. So, I think we should be saying "thank you" daily to them for our care.

Taking the Plunge

ALICIA BRUXVOORT

We celebrated my daughter, Lizzy's, tenth birthday with a splash. Lathered in sunscreen and laden with beach towels, we hauled a mini-van full of kids to a nearby water park for a pool-side party. While the aquatic complex housed snaky waterslides, a walloping wave pool and a sprinkler–studded playground, the highlight of the day loomed four–stories high at the top of a tall timber tower. Though "The Rage" looked as daunting as its name, a steady thread of dripping adventurers wound like a colorful party streamer up the steep wooden stairs. At the pinnacle, bold blue signs invited riders to plummet down a two–hundred foot drop to a small pool at the slide's end.

One by one, my daughter's party guests accepted the spine-tingling challenge. After flinging themselves down the fast and furious fall, they stormed the sundeck where I was enjoying a rare moment of relaxation. And they begged me to join them.

"'Yes, come,' Jesus said. So Peter went over the side of the boat and walked on the water toward Jesus"

MATTHEW 14:29-30, NLT.

"Please, Mom," my birthday girl pleaded. "Come with us this time." I glanced at the sky–high attraction; then at my daughter's hopeful face. Reluctantly, I slipped off my flip flops and headed for "The Rage." Moments later, I stood at the top of the infamous slide and looked down. My stomach flip-flopped as I watched my daughter and her friends speed to the shallow finish. Finally, I was the only one left on the wooden platform.

"Just lie on your back and give yourself a push," the lifeguard instructed as she smacked bubble gum and tediously twirled a silver whistle around her pointer finger. I could see my daughter jumping and clapping at the bottom of the ride as she anticipated my rookie run.

I stepped into the swirling water. *I was enjoying the party from my lawn chair,* I thought. Tentatively, I sat down at the top of the slide. *The water is freezing!* The drop looked daunting from my perspective. One push and I would drop two hundred feet. *Oh, the things we do for our kids.* I took a deep breath (and held it all the way to the bottom), reclined in the cold water; then grabbed the side of the slide. I closed my eyes and pushed my trembling body over the edge.

Water spewed into the air. My heart jumped to my throat. My backside momentarily lifted off the slide and then battered the side wall with a *thump*. Adrenaline rushed. Lizzy screamed with delight. My bulleting body came to a splashing halt.

"You did it, Mom!" Lizzy applauded. "Wasn't that *awesome*?"

As I headed up the steps to do it all over again, I decided that the waterslide was an apt picture of my life with Jesus. Following him is an amazing ride, but sometimes the hardest part is simply taking *the plunge* of obedience.

"I want you and your family to move."

"Are you kidding, Lord? I'm happy right here in my lawn chair. See? I have friends, a great church, a thriving ministry...."

"I want you to surrender your career plans to me."

"But, Lord, I want to pursue *these* dreams..."

"It's time to give your husband the reins. I created him to be the head of your family. Get out of the way and let him become the man I've created him to be."

"But, Lord, he's too busy to lead well. And he doesn't have the vision I do, and...."

And for every argument I have, the Author of this adventure called life urges, "Just take the plunge!"

Hesitantly I push my wary heart over the edge of my comfort zone, and hear my Savior cheer and holler, "Wasn't that an *awesome* ride? How did you like those splashes of joy? Didn't you love that adrenaline pumping rush of dependency on ME? Did you feel your heart lift off the ground and soar?"

As I reach the end of my challenge, I can almost hear Jesus say, "Come on! Let's do it again!"

Really Lord, Her?

CODI JAHN

This was a first. I had never met a "working girl" in person before. She wasn't nearly as glamorous or beautiful as Julia Roberts had been in "Pretty Woman." She was dirty and sloppily dressed. I could smell the lingering scent of cigarettes and alcohol permeating around her like a cloud. Her hands and face looked weathered. I tried not to stare as I walked by her, but I couldn't help myself. What was someone like *her* doing in our office building? I did my best to smile at her, but it was half-hearted. I quickly moved past her and sat down at my desk, hoping she would be gone in a few minutes. Soon my wish was granted and she was out the door.

After she was gone I asked my boss about her. As it turned out she had stopped in briefly to visit him as he was a friend of a friend and she didn't know many people in the area. He didn't seem surprised by the visit or her condition. In his mind she was no different from anyone else. Was I the only one uncomfortable having a "working girl" hang out at our office?

She *was* different from us. Way different. According to my boss, her children had been taken by social services. She had spent years in prison on drug charges. This was all part of a world I couldn't relate to. I sat down at my desk again, unsure why no one else was concerned with this.

"And you also are among those . . . who are called to belong to Jesus Christ" ROMANS 1:6, NIV.

Suddenly it hit me. I felt ashamed as I thought back on the past several minutes. I thought about the parallel. No wonder they hated Jesus. They couldn't understand him. The faithful churchgoers, the Pharisees and Sadducees, must have been blown away by Jesus' willingness to surround himself so closely with people like *her*. I had always thought of the leaders in Jesus day as stuck in religious rut and unwilling to see what was right in front of them, and yet in looking at it, I wasn't so sure I would have been much different.

Jesus challenged norms. He broke tradition. He didn't care what others thought. He viewed all humanity in the same light. He dined with prostitutes, stayed with crooked tax collectors, and hung out with the illiterate. He would have been friends with *her*.

I was a good person! I had attended church regularly my whole life! I donated my time. I donated my money. I loved my neighbor . . . or did I? I thought about the scowl that had suddenly formed on my face when I saw *her*. Then I thought about what it would be like to have her over to my house for dinner.

Weird. As I pictured the scene in my mind, she didn't fit. I imagined awkward silences as we wouldn't have anything in common. It be-

I had never met a "working girl" in person before. She was dirty and sloppily dressed. I could smell the lingering scent of cigarettes and alcohol permeating around her like a cloud.

came easy to see how the religious leaders would have been uncomfortable around Jesus' friends. Forget that they were from a lower caste, maybe outcasts, yet in Jesus mind they all fit under the same one-word description: redeemable. It didn't matter if they were dirty and homeless or religious and wealthy; in his mind, they were redeemable.

I was embarrassed. I had acted so poorly. I claimed to be a Christian and yet when someone didn't fit the mold I expected, I had turned my nose up at them. I learned an important lesson that day, both from our visitor and my non-church going boss who had been a friend to her when I certainly wasn't interested.

"If you love only those who love you, what reward is there for that? Even corrupt tax collectors do that much. If you are kind only to your friends, how are you different from anyone else? Even pagans do that. But you are to be perfect, even as your Father in heaven is perfect" (Matt. 5:46-48, NLT, selected).

I Got You, Girl!

DOROTHY DAVIS

I was excited and giddy about my get-away weekend with my husband. I had made reservations to stay at Yarrow Resort in Michigan. We planned to stay in a cabin and I had made arrangements to have a picnic in the wooded area behind the golf course. I had contacted a close friend to make sure that DJ, our grandson, would be taken care of for worship and dinner.

We decided to leave at 3:00 AM to avoid traffic delays on I-94. I had packed a picnic basket with all of our favorite snacks, sparkling grape juice, and long-stemmed flutes. I had packed my husband's clothes for the trip so there would be one less thing for him to think about.

Before leaving I asked my husband, JD, to leave his cell phone at home because I didn't want any interruptions with our time of renewal. He won the debate by stating we needed to have a means of connecting with DJ if something were to happen while we were away.

"Even when I walk through the darkest valley, I will not be afraid, for you are close beside me" PSALM 23:4, NLT.

I was driving and my husband was relaxing in his seat as we started down the highway. I looked over at him, and as I was checking the mirrors to make sure of the position of the other cars, I heard a loud explosion. My car spun around in the middle of the highway, smashed into the concrete median and did another 360 and stopped on exit ramp 12. It felt as though I was at the State Fair riding in a bumper car. I could hardly breathe; my airbag had deployed and had literally knocked my breath out of me. I kept asking, "What happened?" By this time JD was fully awake and wanted to know if I was all right.

He freed himself from his deployed airbag and opened the door, so he could help me get out of the car. He wanted to know where I was hurt and what had just happened. My response was, "I don't know." A car pulled up behind us and the young couple checked with us to make sure we weren't severely injured. They saw what had happened and they couldn't believe that we were able to walk away from the accident. A driver in a silver car had sped past them going at 90 miles per hour and had

My car spun around in the middle of the highway, smashed into the concrete median and did another 360 and stopped on exit ramp 12.

rammed into the rear of our car, then continued going down the highway. Chelsey, the young lady, asked if she could pray with me while we waited for the medics to come.

She began by saying, "Sovereign God, have mercy on this couple, may their lives be precious in your sight." I believe the angel that has been assigned to me was present with me during that accident. They stayed until the police arrived and gave their eyewitness testimony. The police thought I had fallen asleep at the wheel and the accident was my fault. I thank God that he allowed the angels to remain with us and to be our witnesses.

Fortunately, Jerome did not sustain any visible injuries. I, on the other hand, snapped my collarbone in two places. I was given a sling and medication to help me get through the healing process. Jerome was able to call an elder from our local church to come to the hospital and give us a ride home. I thank God that there are those who were willing to help in our time of emergency.

After looking at the pictures of our totaled car, I realizing that had DJ gone with us, he would have sustained life-threatening injuries because the rear seat was now smashed into our front seats. Our God is an awesome God. We truly passed through the valley of death, but we had no fear because God whispered, "I got you, girl."

Act As If

SARA ALSUP

I was waiting for the left turn arrow early one morning, when I saw it. And I've never seen it again. It was like a "sign" for me. The license tag on the car in front of me said, "ACT AS IF." When I first read it, I was startled with the simple phrase. The more I sat in the line of waiting traffic, the more I puzzled over what the words could possibly mean.

My first inclination was to respond to myself, "What's the point?" I was in such a sleepy state of mind that morning that I wasn't in the mood to think deeply. I just wanted for the green arrow to appear in a hurry and to safely get to work. The longer the light stayed red, the more I couldn't help myself; I mused over and over the phrase, "Act as if."

Then I began to answer the license tag with the first things that popped into my head, like, "Act as if I really believe in God's love; act as if I really trust him; act as if I have great faith; act as if I truly love others."

These lightning quick ideas and themes shocked me! Here I am a Bible teacher telling my students how faithful God is. Now on a Wednesday morning at 7:00 AM I'm trying to convince myself. "What was I thinking? Where were my faith and my trust in the love of God? Where was my thankfulness? Why was I allowing my morning circumstances to dictate how I act

She had been acting as if God was walking with her, sometimes carrying her along the daily path of life.

and feel?" At that moment I was ashamed of my own selfishness and blindness to God.

In the time it took for the red light to change green, these thoughts flew through my mind. I was more perplexed than ever and could hardly keep my mind on work. During break I shared the mystery with the other gals in my office. As I did so, there was complete silence, no response. Their silence bewildered me. So I repeated the concise license message to them, but I was silently asking, "Was the message only for me and for me to discover the true meaning?"

At the point of hush, a new employee timidly raised her hand and began to explain that her life recently took an unexpected turn. Now this young gal was viewed as shy and perhaps a little standoffish. She began to tell us her very own personal dilemma. With tiny tears threatening to roll from her round brown eyes, she acknowledge that she believed God was still in control of her very life and he still loved her—regardless of her personal suffering. None of us had any inkling of the secret pain she endured. "Why is this, I asked myself?" The clear answer is that she had been *acting as if* God was walking with her, sometimes carrying her along the daily path of life.

She got it! Her outlook showed she understood God's love and care, and her life showed only his grace.

My outlook was changed in moments of meaningful messages from the One who loves me most.

Because of her personal outlook on God's grace for her, I felt the emotion of being ashamed of my own fragment of faith. From this moment and during the day, I reflected on how many times and ways God had showed me his love and grace. Early that morning he had told me to "Get up." The next communication was when I saw the rectangular license plate message. Thirdly was the sweet voice of my coworker.

How could I doubt for one minute God's love and care for my life! How could I challenge his unfailing love?

Renewed with the blessed encouragements that God had sent to me, I picked myself up and put a thankful smile on my face and into my heart and moved on with considerable faith, trust, and love. My outlook was changed in moments of meaningful messages from the One who loves me most.

"You have persevered and have endured hardships for my name, and have not grown weary. Yet I hold this against you: You have forsaken the love you had at first. Consider how far you have fallen! Repent and do the things you did at first..." (Rev. 3: 2-5, NIV).

Are you Afraid?

JOANNE CORTES

Jesus loves me this I know, for the Bible tells me so. Little ones to him belong, they are weak but he is strong. Yes, Jesus loves me. Yes, Jesus loves me. Yes, Jesus loves me. The Bible tells me so."

I remember as a child, there were times I would wake up in the middle of the night, scared, fearful, because of a bad dream. It was hard going back to sleep after dreaming that a big monster was chasing me. I would toss and turn, asking God to catch that big monster and throw him far, far away so he would not bother me again, so I could sleep through the night. Every time I felt afraid, I would sing "Jesus loves me, this I know." I would sing it over and over, until I eventually fell asleep.

Singing this song always brought me peace. I knew that whenever that imaginary big monster would come to bother me, Jesus, who loved me, was stronger and bigger, and I felt safe knowing that I belonged to him and no monster, no matter how big and scary, could harm me. Even now, when at times I might be anxious, or afraid, I sing this song and it gives me the assurance that everything is going to be okay, because I know, Jesus loves me!

"For I am the LORD your God who takes hold of your right hand and says to you, Do not fear; I will help you"

ISAIAH 41:13, NIV.

Last night, I woke up to the cries of my son Jose. I ran to his room and asked him what was happening. Half asleep, he started talking to me about flying mushrooms and turtles that were chasing him. He was afraid they were going to catch him. All he kept saying was "Mama, they are going to get me, they are going to get me." I realized he was having a bad dream and was taken back to my childhood days. I assured him that everything would be ok and began to sing "Jesus loves me this I know." When I finished the song, he requested that I sing it again… and again. I sang until he peacefully dozed off, affirming once more that singing to Jesus when you are afraid and during times of distress, brings peace and helps to overcome fear.

Is there something that you're afraid of? Are you anxious about tomorrow? Is there a "monster," something that is keeping you far from your lifetime dreams and aspirations? Is there someone who is hurting you? Do you have fears that won't let you sleep?

Remember, Jesus loves you! He does not want you to be afraid or anxious. He has promised that he will be with you always and will give you the strength and courage to face any "monster" that may come your way.

It was hard going back to sleep after dreaming that a big monster was chasing me. I would toss and turn, asking God to catch that big monster and throw him far, far away so he would not bother me again, so I could sleep through the night.

God promises to hold your hand through any of life's circumstances. He says "Do not fear, I am with you." He was with David when facing Goliath; with the three Hebrew boys in the fiery furnace; with Daniel in the lions' den; with Esther when she had to go before the King; with Mary, a virgin who was chosen to carry the Son of God; with the disciples on the boat in the midst of a storm. And he is with you today.

Next time flying mushrooms, turtles or monsters of life chase after you and you don't know what to do or say, remember that you are not alone, and don't forget to sing, "Yes Jesus loves me...."

"For I am the LORD your God who takes hold of your right hand and says to you, Do not fear; I will help you" (Isaiah 41:13, NIV).

Prayer: Lord, You know my fears and anxieties. Please help me to trust in you. I know you will rescue and deliver me from any "monster."

Craft Night

Jenni Glass

As I pulled into my driveway, a wave of anxiety fell over me. I suddenly had a feeling that I had to be somewhere but had forgotten when and where. As someone who lives by a calendar would do, I panicked. I was certain that I had double checked my calendar earlier in the day as I thought about what I was going to do when I got home that evening. I checked my calendar on my phone and sure enough, there was nothing listed.

So why did I have this feeling that I was supposed to be somewhere? Then it hit me. It was Tuesday. That is when the tears started to stream down my face and memories flooded to my mind. Tuesday was "Craft Night." For me, Tuesday will always be craft night.

Best I can remember it started when my friend Tara and I were talking one day and she asked if I would like to come over for dinner on Tuesday night while her husband was at orchestra practice. Without hesitation I said, "Yes." I learned early on in our friendship that I should never turn down a meal at Tara's house. She is an amazing cook, and as a single female I hated to cook for one. Plus she always sent me home with lunch for the next day. She also mentioned to me about bringing over some crocheting or knitting to work on after dinner. Thus began a wonderful tradition of Craft Night.

"There are 'friends' who destroy each other, but a real friend sticks closer than a brother"

PROVERBS 18:24, NLT.

Craft Night went on for many years. Periodically others would join us, but more often than not, it was just Tara and me. I learned to knit and improved my crocheting skills over the years. I even learned to sew, yet to this day my mom still doesn't believe that I know how to use a sewing machine. We talked a lot during these nights. Some nights were light-hearted and others were filled with tears as we discussed our jobs, families, friends, likes, dislikes, the future, and the list goes on. No topic was off limits.

In my mind, Craft Night would always exist. I couldn't imagine life without Craft Night. Then the news came. Tara told me that her husband had accepted a new job and they were moving to California. My heart sunk. My best friend was going to move 1,800 miles away. Even though I knew this was in God's plan, I was still sad.

That night in the driveway I realized that although we didn't live close to each other anymore, Craft Night would continue in my heart and mind. I also realized how blessed I was to have those many years of Craft Night to form such a strong bond with a friend. I don't have a sister, but I believe God blessed me with a sister named Tara.

Shortly after that night in my driveway, Tara and I were chatting via Web cam. I began to chuckle as I realized she was cooking and I was sewing as we talked, our first Virtual Craft Night. I made my first trip out to California

Tuesday was "Craft Night." For me, Tuesday will always be craft night.

about three months after Tara moved. For old time's sake, we set one night aside for Craft Night. As I sat at the sewing machine and Tara knitted a hat, my heart leaped for joy that Craft Night would always be a part of my life.

Epilogue: A few years have passed since Tara moved to California. I have learned in these past few years that some projects just require two people. During my last trip to California we worked on a purse project together that we started before she moved. I just can't bring myself to finish the project without her. So the project sits in my craft room waiting for Tara to come to Kansas City for a visit. Maybe I will actually get to use the purse next time I fly out to California.

"There are 'friends' who destroy each other, but a real friend sticks closer than a brother" (Proverbs 18:24, NLT).

The Gift of Trust

EVE RUSK

It was already an extraordinary Thanksgiving weekend. My husband and I had traveled from Idaho to Arizona and Southern California to finalize his father's estate. Thanksgiving dinner was in a restaurant. While the food was good, the atmosphere just didn't resonate. It certainly wasn't home. Still, we were thankful to have something, since the friends we were staying with that evening already had other plans.

We arrived home after a long drive to find a voicemail message and a letter from the mammography center I had visited just ten days before for my annual screening. The letter said that something had been discovered that required further diagnostic tests and to please call and make an appointment. When I called, the receptionist was very encouraging, saying that 80 percent of these findings turn out to be nothing. I knew, though, that this was not "nothing."

"But those who hope in the Lord will renew their strength. They will soar on wings like eagles; they will run and not grow weary, they will walk and not be faint" ISAIAH 40:31, NIV.

"It looks suspicious, so we want to do a biopsy." Somewhere deep in me, those words caused terror. But outwardly, I was calm. My biopsy was scheduled for a Friday afternoon. The following Sunday was my husband's office Christmas party. It was surreal, being there in festive dress, surrounded by coworkers and their families, singing Christmas carols, eating delicious food. Outwardly, I was calm and trusting. Inside, my mind was racing. *It's probably cancer. How can I get this taken care of and still take care of my family, especially my granddaughter, who lives with us? How bad is it going to be?*

The radiologist told me he would have the results by Tuesday evening. So when the phone rang at 9 AM Tuesday, I was unprepared. Yes, it was cancer. But it was small and didn't appear to have spread.

Then the whirlwind started. Set up blood work and chest X-ray and surgical consultation. "You're so young—only forty-nine," I heard many times. Did I have any questions? I could only think of a few. I was still outwardly calm, but inside, my mind was racing again. That night, I wasn't feeling well, so I took my blood pressure: 190 over 110. Definitely not healthy. My fear that night wasn't about the cancer, but about having a stroke. I prayed to God that he would keep me alive and calm me. I was no longer outwardly calm.

My blood pressure lowered some the next day, but I went to see a doctor about it. I was an emotional mess. This wasn't the only stressful thing in my life that year. Of the major stress events, we had experienced several within a six-month period. The doctor recognized the load I was carrying and gave me something to help. It allowed my mind to slow down, to recognize that I needed help from others, and from God.

Two days before Christmas, I had a lumpectomy. I wasn't calm—I was scared. I knew God would be with me, that he was in control, but I was still scared. I think that's okay. It gave others the opportunity to minister to me. I am a person who gets things done. I like being in control of situations. Often, the easiest way to get something accomplished was to do it myself. So this situation wasn't "me." I don't like to depend on others.

After surgery and six and a half weeks of radiation treatment, I was definitely cancer-free. Wonderful words to hear. But at that point, I didn't need those words to calm me, to encourage me, to give me hope. My aunt suggested a web site that would allow me to post updates and readers could post messages to me. I had found it through the words and prayers of countless people who took the time to read my updates, to encourage me, and to let me know that their prayer group was praying for me. Knowing that strengthened my trust in God. I learned to trust others more, to be vulnerable, to accept help. God is good—all the time.

Trust is not a finite thing. It grows like faith. The ability to trust is a gift from God, just like faith. Don't worry if you feel you can't trust fully. God will provide what you need to get you through.

Because He Paid for Me

CARMALITA GREEN

I have this habit that I've picked up from one of my parents (my mother made me promise not to tell which parent). I like to make sure I get my money's worth out of all my purchases. I consider this to be an honorable quality; however, it does from time to time cause me to expend more energy and invest more time than the original product cost.

Recently, I found myself struggling to get the last bit of toothpaste out of the toothpaste tube. Normally this would not be a problem but this particular morning I was walking a fine line to almost being late for work. As I stood in the bathroom squeezing the life out of my toothpaste tube, I questioned myself as to why I didn't just throw that almost, basically empty tube of toothpaste away and grab the full tube in the cabinet. After all it would save much needed time. My response was, "Because I paid for it, every bit of toothpaste in that tube is mine, and it is valuable to me, and I'm not throwing it away." And in that very moment the Holy Spirit said, "Exactly."

"For ye are bought with a price: therefore glorify God in your body, and in your spirit, which are God's"

1 CORINTHIANS 6:20, KJV.

That may seem like a strange response, but really, it's not. See, I have a hard time understanding God's unconditional love for me. It is like trying to use software for a Mac on a PC.

It just does not compute. Every time I input unconditional love into my mind, I get an error message. I often find myself having a conversation with God that goes a little like this: "God why do you continue to allow me to live? As sinful as I am, after all the times I have asked forgiveness for a particular sin only to do it again why do you allow me to live? Why don't you just throw me away? You must have other children who love and obey you more than I."

In order to help me understand, God uses objects and situations I do understand and know to teach me about his unconditional love. Money is something I know and understand. I understand that I do not have a lot of money. I understand how hard I have to work to earn money. I understand that money is spent faster than it is earned. And I understand that it is not only profitable but necessary to get the most out of everything that I purchase because it is mine, I not only invested money but also time in acquiring it, so I want the best from it.

The same can be said of God's longsuffering with me. God sent his only Son from the glory of heaven to earth to die the death that

I like to make sure I get my money's worth out of all my purchases. I consider this to be an honorable quality; however, it does from time to time cause me to expend more energy and invest more time than the original product cost.

should have been mine. In addition to loving me unconditionally, he paid for me with the blood of his Son. I belong to him, every bit of me, and he will not throw me away. Therefore, he takes the time to mold me, yes even squeeze me into his image. Instead of throwing me away every time I mess up he will continue to work on me, scrubbing and buffing away layers of sin and filth until I am all he created me to be, until I reflect his image. It does not matter how long he has to work on me or that he will expend more time and energy than the original product cost. Because God loves me and is able to save to the uttermost, he will continue to work on me.

Why does God love me so? Because he paid for me.

"For ye are bought with a price: therefore glorify God in your body, and in your spirit, which are God's" (1 Corinthians 6:20, KJV).

Confessions of a *Culinary Klutz*

JAMIE SANTA CRUZ

*H*aving grown up with a mother who served up delicious, healthy, home-cooked meals as the daily fare for our family, you'd think I would have learned a thing or two about good cooking. Sadly, however, none of mom's culinary skills rubbed off on me. When I moved out on my own at 24, my competence in the kitchen was, well, non-existent.

I still remember the first time I invited a friend over for a homemade lunch. A few days in advance, I decided on a menu—salad, potato soup, and biscuits—and called my mom for recipes. Then, shopping list in hand, I headed to the grocery store for ingredients. On the day of the lunch, I set out all my ingredients on the counter an hour before my friend was to arrive, propped up my printout of Mom's e-mailed recipes, and got to work.

It was a disaster.

"Sauté onion in oil," was step number one for the soup. I had no idea what a sautéed onion was supposed to look like. I dropped the diced onion into a pot, set it on a warm burner, then dutifully stood guard over the pot, poking it every few seconds with my long-handled wooden spoon, nervously wondering how long was this sautéing process was supposed to take, anyway.

"One tablespoon fresh parsley," read the recipe. Lacking the fresh herbs, I tossed in a tablespoon

"So whether you eat or drink or whatever you do, do all to the glory of God"

1 CORINTHIANS 10:31, NIV.

of dried parsley instead. Then I noticed the equivalency directions on the side of the parsley jar: "1 teaspoon dried parsley = 1 tablespoon fresh parsley." Oops.

"Bake until lightly browned," I read in Mom's directions for the biscuits, so when I pulled the biscuits out of the oven after fourteen minutes, I agonized over whether or not my floured rounds had achieved the proper color. Gingerly lifting the biscuits off the baking sheet with a spatula, I tested one with my finger. Light and fluffy as…rawhide.

My friend was kind and said nothing about the biscuits-that-could-have-been-paperweights or the still-crunchy potatoes swimming in parsley broth. But it was months before I worked up the nerve to invite anyone over for a meal again. For two years, any time I took a dish to a potluck, I panicked over whether or not my offering tasted "normal," and I'd nervously eye each guest as they went through the food line, painfully sensitive to whether or not someone passed over my contribution and to how much of my dish was left over at the end of the meal.

But despite my apprehension about cooking, I persisted. I pored over cookbooks, studying them for hints and tips on how to bake sandwich bread or form a pie crust. I regularly called my mom to ask about such things as how to steam broccoli or what "al dente" means. And I practiced.

Eventually, the persistence paid off. I learned how to sauté an onion and how to make fluffy biscuits. I began coming home from potlucks with bowls scraped clean, rather than with most of my contribution left untouched in the dish. And one day, after I'd finally risked inviting some friends over for soup again, I was shocked and thrilled when one guest actually asked for my recipe!

Today, being asked for recipes is no longer unusual, and I no longer feel anxious about hosting a meal. I've even developed a specialty in healthy, plant-based cooking, and my ongoing ambition in the kitchen is to see how many vegetables or whole grains I can sneak into a dish without anyone realizing they are actually eating something healthy. (Since even my husband, not a healthy eater before he married me, claims he loves my cooking, apparently my mission has been somewhat successful.)

Learning to cook—and especially learning to cook healthy meals—is no easy task. But knowing that I am able to contribute to the long-term health of my family through nutritious cooking is definitely worth the effort. And my story goes to show that anyone—even the clueless!—can do it successfully.

Follow the Plan!

Delores Francois

I left my doctor's office late one afternoon in December with a mandate to lose weight. This was not the first time the doctor had suggested I lose weight. But I had been having a hard time trying to get fully motivated to do something about it. This time she strongly suggested I lose the weight or suffer the health consequences. There was my motivation!

I set my goal. I would lose twenty pounds. Now I needed a plan. My office just happened to begin a "Biggest Loser" contest. The contest began in February and was to end in late April. I joined. I decided I would exercise, modify my diet, and drink lots and lots of water in order to achieve my goal by the end of the contest. With my plan mapped out, I was ready to put it in action!

I began briskly walking four miles each morning before I went to work. The mornings were very cold and a few mornings there was snow! In the beginning I hated getting out of my warm bed, and some days I didn't quite make it. However, I kept reminding myself of my goal and how much better I would look and feel.

I set my goal. I would lose twenty pounds. Now I needed a plan.

I gave up the sweet stuff during the week, the snacks and soft drinks in the afternoons. I started drinking lots of water. I learned to stick to only one helping of food and smaller portions at mealtimes. As the weeks went by the weight slowly started coming off. I did have some set-backs; however, I kept my goal in mind and persevered.

I had a very good support and encouragement system in place. My brother would call me twice a week to encourage me to stick with the plan. My husband stopped filling the kitchen panty with all the goodies we liked so that I would not be tempted. My coworkers and my girlfriends would notice and comment on how nice I was slimming down.

On the final day of the contest, I weighed in with a loss of 18.2 pounds! Even though I missed my goal by two pounds, I considered it a big success! I won the contest! I lost the highest percentage of weight in the contest! All my hard work had paid off! I felt physically better than I had felt in years! What a great feeling! I had followed the plan.

My action plan put me on the road to physical wellness. As a Christian, I need to have an action plan for my mental and spiritual wellness. I have set my goal. I want to be within God's will for my life and to meet him in heaven. My plan is to consistently exercise the privilege of prayer and to faithfully study God's Word. Putting the plan in action, I will reflect God's unselfish love to mankind. I will solicit the support of good Christian friends who will help me stay focused. There will be days that I will miss the mark; however, I will not give up. I will ask God for his forgiveness, grace, and mercy. People will look at me and say, "Wow, there is something special about her." They will see my spiritual beauty. Why? Because I will follow the plan!

God also had a plan. It was called the plan of redemption. It pretty much was the biggest plan the world has ever known. We are so blessed and privileged to have had a plan so beautifully and lovingly prepared for us! God's goal was to redeem fallen humanity. The plan was to send his only begotten Son, Jesus, to a sinful world. God put the plan in action at the birth of Jesus, his death at Calvary, his resurrection, and ultimately his second coming. Oh, and by the way, he sent some support and encouragement through the presence of his Holy Spirit. He could have changed his mind when he foresaw all the things that were going to happen to his precious Son. He didn't. What love! I've been redeemed because he followed the plan!

"For I know the plans I have for you ..." (Jeremiah 29:11, NIV).

The Tender Trust of Life

COLLENE KELLY

The fat, translucent orange caterpillar crawled across the back patio. Spying it, my seven-year daughter triumphantly captured her prize and displayed it to one after another of the family members. Though we had hatched several butterflies over the summer, this one looked different than all the others.

We'd captured the striped Monarch caterpillars in our garden, and observed the transformational process unfold before our eyes. Each vivid green chrysalis turned nearly black before it split, and out emerged a wet-winged butterfly. The kids held the new creation carefully, the thread-like legs of the Monarch clinging to their fingers. The long, black tongue, fragile as spider's legs, uncurled, and we watched with delight as the insect drank our homemade nectar from a cotton ball.

Each vivid green chrysalis turned nearly black before it split, and out emerged a wet-winged butterfly. The kids held the new creation carefully, the thread-like legs of the Monarch clinging to their fingers.

We watched as each butterfly alternately pumped blood through their wet wings, and then rested. Soon they were able to fly, and our hearts soared with them as we released them into the summer sunshine. One of the beautiful insects' wings was crumpled, and Julie babied along "Heather," as she named her. Since she only walked, Heather spent most of her time in the cardboard box, when she wasn't being carried around. One warm day as the kids played on the porch, Heather flitted up and away, and we rejoiced she'd conquered her handicap.

But a more unusual caterpillar arrested our attention. It was late in the season, and cool weather flirted with the waning summer sun. Even if we saved the unique specimen, would there be flowers sufficient to provide for its sustenance when it hatched? We confined it in our canning jar "incubator," and after several days, a brown chrysalis replaced the caterpillar. For several months, nothing happened, and eventually I placed the jar on a shelf beside the basement steps.

In the very depths of the February freeze, Julie discovered the chrysalis open, and a new butterfly in the jar. With squeals of unequaled delight she brought the stunning Swallowtail to me. Soon it flitted across our living room, its iridescent wings catching the sunshine streaming in the window. Knowing it had no chance to survive the frigid outdoors, we boiled a new batch of nectar and soaked several fluffy cotton balls.

But despite our best efforts, this gorgeous,

Life is a tender trust. We can take it, but we can't make it. It is a gift. The timeless proverb, "Teaching a child not to step on a caterpillar is as valuable to the child as it is to the caterpillar," still rings true.

out-of-season insect refused our offerings. A couple days later Julie came to me, her chest heaving with sobs of a broken heart, and tears racing down her cheeks. Our butterfly was dead. I comforted her the best I could, assuring her that she had done everything possible to save the gilded insect. Julie chose a wooden box, and tenderly placed the butterfly on the scarlet lining, a lesson in life and loving, tucked in her young heart.

Life is a tender trust. We can take it, but we can't make it. It is a gift. The timeless proverb, "Teaching a child not to step on a caterpillar is as valuable to the child as it is to the caterpillar," still rings true.

Someday soon there will be new heavens and a new earth. Until then we must teach our children to respect the gift of life, whether in the person of a classmate, or in a fat, orange caterpillar crawling across the patio.

"A righteous man regards the life of his animal; but the tender mercies of the wicked are cruel" (Proverbs 12:10, NKJV).

If Today
Is All I Have

LINDA NORDYKE HAMBLETON

I'm happiest when I wake up breathing. I am acutely aware of the exchange of air through the lungs, the pulsating movement of blood in a vein, the billions of electric impulses that form a thought in the mind. Life is an amazing gift.

There was a time—long ago—when such things were taken for granted. Somewhere, on the edge of my memory, I can vaguely recall days when these activities took place unnoticed and unappreciated. It was a time when my body served me like a faithful assistant: It took me where I wanted to go; it did what I asked; and it communicated what I wanted to say. It was a short season when my body functioned more or less without effort—days when superficial whims and desires could nudge me to and fro. I was healthy; my soul free, my thoughts drifting like a toy boat dancing with the breeze.

And then it all evaporated like a mirage in the desert of reality. Yes, I am happiest when I wake up breathing. But today, each breath has a price; each hour costs; each day is expensive. Today the blood still pulsates, but every beat of my heart depends on a delicate balance of needles and pills.

I am happiest when I wake up breathing. But today, each breath has a price; each hour costs; each day is expensive.

Each day is a complex series of steps in an intricate dance to maintain life—a dance that my doctors, family and

167

I share together. The breathing continues, but basic bodily functions are sustained by machines, a sacrificial family, and teams of medical experts. Thoughts still form in my brain, but they are focused and strategic since clear thinking is necessary for physical survival now. And when it comes time to move, every movement is preceded by careful planning and a concerted, intentional, conscious focus of my will. A growing percentage of my day (much more than half now) is spent in bed, in pain and, at times . . . in fear.

"Life" is an amazing gift. I am more convinced of that now than ever before. But as M. Scott Peck wrote in the opening words of *The Road Less Traveled*: Life is difficult.

Certainly, simple numbers cannot define us, yet the statistics that describe our lives have a story to tell. Here are a few of mine. Since contracting my disease, I have experienced:

- 128 hospitalizations
- 6.75 average days per hospitalization
- 37,500 shots
- 2 organ transplants
- 69-74 pills/day, or about 168,000 total
- 2 heart attacks
- 3 cardiac arrests
- 3 strokes
- 250 grand mal seizures and about 150 focal seizures
- 12,000 laser blasts to my eyes
- 52 inches of incisions, 255 stitches and 137 titanium staples

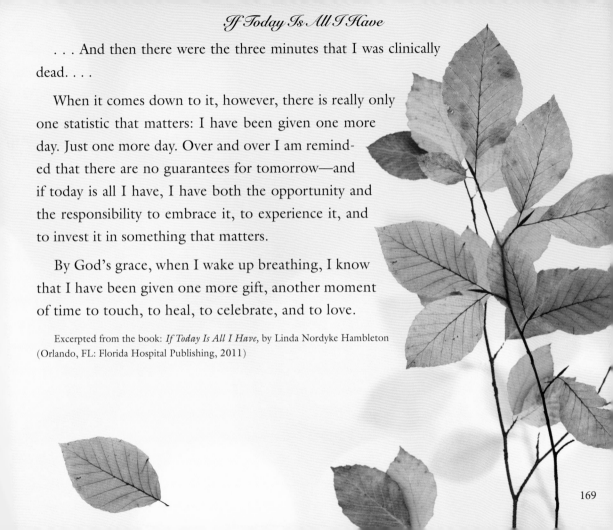

. . . And then there were the three minutes that I was clinically dead. . . .

When it comes down to it, however, there is really only one statistic that matters: I have been given one more day. Just one more day. Over and over I am reminded that there are no guarantees for tomorrow—and if today is all I have, I have both the opportunity and the responsibility to embrace it, to experience it, and to invest it in something that matters.

By God's grace, when I wake up breathing, I know that I have been given one more gift, another moment of time to touch, to heal, to celebrate, and to love.

Excerpted from the book: *If Today Is All I Have,* by Linda Nordyke Hambleton (Orlando, FL: Florida Hospital Publishing, 2011)

The Magic of Believing

DR. LORRAINE JAMES-STIGGERS

*E*very day of the week, every week of the month, and every month of the year is busy and challenging for me as a wife, mother, educator, counselor, and therapist. I thank the Lord each morning he allows me to experience his miracle working power.

One summer morning, I lay in bed trying to decide if I should get up to attend a meeting or stay in bed for just a few more minutes to rest. I remained in bed for a short while and then tried lifting my head off the pillow, my usual routine, but to my surprise I was unable to move it. After several unsuccessful attempts to lift my head, roll out, turn over or to move any part of my body, I finally realized something was seriously wrong. I lay still, looking up at the ceiling wondering, *How in the world did I get myself in this situation?* Fear swept over me as tears streamed down my face into my ears.

After several unsuccessful attempts to lift my head, roll out, turned over or to move any part of my body, I finally realized something was seriously wrong.

My husband was in another room on the other side of the house, but I was reluctant to accept the possible response he might have given so I remained still and waited. I prayed, "Lord, what should I do now? You have my undivided attention."

In a still small voice, Jesus whispered, "Have faith, I promised you that I will never leave you or forsake you. I am here. I will restore."

With those words of comfort and assurance lingering in my ears, an indescribable calm and peace embraced me and I rested in his loving arms. I was no longer angry, impatient, fearful, frustrated, and bewildered but relaxed, knowing that he was in control.

I have always been extremely active and involved in community service and ministry, participating in community outreach programs, ingathering, church school events, walk for diabetes, drug free marches, as a volunteer for the Red Cross, and much more. Playing tennis, bike riding, running, travelling, swimming, reading, walking, teaching, sewing, and writing have been some of my favorite pastime activities but never did I ever imagine, in my wildest dreams, that I would be unable to move when I wanted or need to move.

My husband eventually assisted me to get some much needed help that I was more than willing to receive. I learned that my kidneys had failed. Water wasn't one of my favorite beverages. Saying "NO" when I was already overwhelmed and exhausted was difficult for me. Eating meals at the same time every day seemed virtually impossible due to my unpredictable schedule. Making sure that I got adequate amounts of rest was challenging. All of these things had contributed to my present state. And all of them had to change.

The Lord wishes above all things that we "prosper in all things and be in health, just as your soul prospers," as John wrote (3 JOHN 1:2, NKJV).

This experience led me to commit to taking better care of my health in a holistic way, encompassing the body, mind, and spirit. Even though I currently have 60 percent of kidney functioning, the Lord is keeping his promise when he told me, "I will restore." He is doing that each and every day of my life. The Lord is continually working miracles in my life, one indicator being I am still here. He is my Restorer, my Healer, my Protector, my Comforter, my Redeemer, my Provider, my "Everything." Remember, the Lord wishes above all things that we *"prosper in all things and be in health, just as your soul prospers,"* as John wrote (3 John 1:2, NKJV).

And he wants us to believe, even when things may seem impossible: *"…for assuredly, I say to you, if you have faith as a mustard seed, you will say to this mountain 'Move from here to there,' and it will move; and nothing will be impossible for you"* (Matthew 17:20, NKJV).

On Eagles' Wings

FRANCES MORFORD

*S*lamming the car door, I ran into the house. "Monroe has to go register the car and I'll finish packing. Is there anything I can do to help while he is gone?" I inquired.

"You can turn off the beans," my sister replied. I ran into the kitchen and immediately slipped and crashed onto my left ankle. There was a slight click and a stabbing pain. "Oh, no!" my sister cried. "I just mopped the floor and it is still wet." Strong arms gently picked me up and carried me to the front room couch.

When my husband returned four hours later, he found a tear-stained wife reclining on the couch with an ankle propped up on an ice pack. "What happened?" he asked. I tried to explain, but sobs shook me as I realized the problem this accident was causing.

We had been spending weeks getting shots, and so forth in preparation for me to return to the mission field with my husband. Now that exciting bubble had broken along with my ankle. Buckets of tears started flowing again.

He was returning to South Sudan in just a few weeks. This would drastically change plans. Monroe was only home on a short furlough and I was planning to return with him. There was no choice. He had to return. We had been spending weeks getting shots, and so forth in preparation for me to return with him. Now that exciting bubble had broken along with my ankle. Buckets of tears started flowing again.

"Let's get you to the doctor and get his advice. Then we will know how to proceed," my patient, not easily shaken husband said as he loaded me into the car. Of course, after the X-ray and all the advice, we had to change plans. I had to stay off my ankle for six weeks. He had to go back to Sudan without me again.

My broken ankle healed quickly as I waited week after week in my Lazy-boy chair, reading and praying. One night I came across Isaiah 40:31. *"But they that wait upon the Lord shall renew their strength; they shall mount up with wings like eagles; they shall run and not be weary; and they shall walk, and not faint" (KJV)*. As I was pondering those words, the phone rang.

"Hello, this is the church Conference. We are making arrangements for your flight to South Sudan. Your passport and tickets should arrive within a couple of days. The itinerary is all made out for you to meet your husband. Call if you have any questions or problems." What a relief. I really had nothing to fear.

Soon, however, I was faced with decisions I had never had to handle before. Fear took over. We had travelled overseas many times, but my capable, self-confident husband had always taken care of things while I just tagged along watching the luggage. *How do I pack so I won't be overweight, get to the airport and locate the right ticket window?* I wondered. But most of all I realized that although I could walk on my ankle again, how could I carry all my bags and make it through the terminals alone? Panic took over again. My sister reminded me that airlines offered wheelchair assistance. They would take care of me all the way. Another answer to prayer!

When the day arrived, I snapped the lock on the last tightly packed bag, picked up my purse bulging with the important passport, tickets, and other needed items. As I locked the door behind me, I bowed my head in a short prayer, then jammed the oversized baggage in the trunk of my sister's car, picked up my hand luggage, crawled into the back seat, and shut the door.

As the airplane seat belt snapped around my waist, I settled down to relax. The fear that had been gnawing inside left and I began to recall all that had happened in the last few months. God had been so good. He had given me the opportunity to read my Bible and find Scriptures that strengthened my faith while I was recuperating. I had witnessed miracles happening almost daily. I remember reading Isaiah 41:10: *"Don't be afraid, for I am with you. Don't be discouraged, for I am your God. I will strengthen you and help you"* (NLT). Now I felt ready to spend time in our new mission field. My strength had been renewed. I could walk and I was even flying on eagle wings. What a wonderful God!

For Melinda

GLADYS JOY! BAZEMORE

I couldn't find a particular mobile home park, so I started knocking, to see a few more people before dark. Melinda opened her door and greeted me. She asked, "Who are you and where are you from?" I held out a flyer and said, "I'm with the Bible Story, those blue books you see in the doctor's office. Have you seen those before?" "Oh, yes," she said. "Would you like to come in and get out of this heat?" We sat down at her kitchen table, and she asked, "Haven't we met somewhere before? You just look so familiar!" She said she had the books years ago. "But my brother has them for his kids now, and I know I'll get them back for my grandchildren later," she finished. She did not want to look at big books today.

"Let me show you something really nice that we have," I said, pulling out some of our books—*My Friend Jesus, Storybook, Peace above the Storm, God's Answers, Foods That Heal*. As Melinda glanced through *Foods That Heal*, she said, "This is good. I'm a nurse, so I'm familiar with some of this." She told me which doctor she worked for, and I said, "Oh, I've been going in there for the last twelve years to check your *Bible Story* book!"

About three years earlier her husband and son-in-law had been killed in a boating accident. They had gone fishing for the day and ended up drowned.

Melinda laughed, "That's where I've seen you before. That's why you look familiar!"

When I asked if she would like to give a donation for some of the books, she gave a strong, "Yes!" and went to get her checkbook.

Then she asked, "Do you have a few minutes? May I share something with you?" She left the kitchen and came back, clutching something to her heart. "I share this story whenever I can," she began. About three years earlier her husband and son-in-law had been killed in a boating accident. They had gone fishing for the day and ended up drowned. In fact, the son-in-law was lost under the water for ten days, and they had the funeral for her husband, not knowing if they would ever find the son-in-law. A year later she said she just wanted to get away for a while. So she and her two grown daughters and their little children went to their time-share vacation spot in another country.

On the very day of the anniversary of her loss, she was walking the beach alone, drawing hearts on the sand and bawling her heart out to God, grieving her dear husband of thirty years. Suddenly, a wave swept up something at her feet. She reached down to grasp it quickly. It was a piece of shell or worn coral, smoothed by waves and sand into a beautiful little heart. She stared at it in her hand, praising God through her tears that he had remembered her.

"No tears are shed that God does not notice. There is no smile that He does not mark...." PEACE ABOVE THE STORM

"And here it is," she finished as she handed me

180

the frame. There was the little heart, mounted behind glass.

She told me, "I don't understand God's will, but I believe that he has used me through it all."

She started a widow's support group. As she waited for the ladies to come for the first meeting she could see her own shadow on the wall, and she thought, *How can this be? How can I be a widow? I was supposed to retire in just a few years and just enjoy life together with him.* Then she said, "Other people have told me that they have taken courage in difficulties because they say, 'If Melinda can hold up under what she's been through, we can make it through this.'"

I read to her from *Peace Above the Storm*, where it says: "No tears are shed that God does not notice. There is no smile that He does not mark...." When I looked up, Melinda said, "I can't wait to start reading!"

We prayed together before I left, and I knew I had been sent down that road, not for a mobile home park, but for Melinda.

Safe as a Deer

LISA CLOUZET

*I*f you live here long enough, you will hit a deer," was the warning I received from more than one person after moving to rural Michigan. I had heard horror stories of deer jumping out onto the highway and causing accidents. It seemed that every other week—at certain times of the year more than others—the local paper reported on deer-versus-car incidents. I often spotted deer alone or in small herds while driving along the highway. Most of the ones I spotted were dead alongside the road. I knew that dawn and dusk were the times to be especially alert. I have to admit that I had probably become a little paranoid about driving at those times of day.

I had not driven more than three miles when I spotted the deer. The highway light acted as a spotlight shining down through the fog and I immediately slowed down, noting there was an exit I could use to avoid hitting the deer.

So, as I headed for the airport, I prayed for protection. "Lord, please protect the deer and me from each other!" I guided my car through the early morning darkness, fog, and snow flurries onto the highway entrance ramp. Michigan winter driving conditions added to the anxiety I felt about making my flight on time.

I had not driven more than three miles when I spotted the deer. The highway light acted as a spotlight shining down through the fog and I immediately slowed down, noting there was an exit I could use to avoid hitting the deer. Just as I was beginning to steer onto the exit ramp, the deer began moving away from my lane and off to the other side of the road.

I could hear my heart pounding in my ears as I sent up an audible "Thank You" and continued on my way.

I made my flight and arrived safely at the airport in another state where my husband was waiting for me. On the way to where we were to spend the night, I was sharing my deer encounter experience with him. A few minutes later, a large deer came running out into the five-lane freeway, heading straight for us! Miraculously, it had avoided being hit on its way to our lane and then—almost as if it were held forcibly back right at our lane— it suddenly turned on its heels and ran back across the four lanes and into the woods. I am not sure if the deer could have been more frightened than we were!

I felt goose bumps as the realization hit me—there was no mistake—there was not one light along that section of highway! Today, I am convinced that the "spotlight" came from a heavenly source rather than from a highway light.

Once again, I sent up a "Thank You."

A few days later, as my husband and I drove home from our Michigan airport, I wanted to identify at which exit I had seen the deer. I figured it would be easy since the first few exits had no highway lights. Imagine my amazement when I had passed all the exits and not one had a light. I had no doubt that my prayer had been answered, but I thought I had just missed the light, so I paid special attention the next time I made the same trip. I felt goose bumps as the realization hit me—there was no mistake—there was not one light along that section of highway! Today, I am convinced that the "spotlight" came from a heavenly source rather than from a highway light.

I still live in Michigan and travel the same highways. I still have a healthy respect for the many deer that I know are out there. I still say a prayer for the Lord to protect the deer and me from each other, assured that he continues to hear and answer.

"When I am afraid, I put my trust in you" (Psalm 56:3, NIV).

Lazarus
the Cat

Lisa Harper

One bright summer day, a tiny orange tabby appeared on the rock wall outside my bedroom and smiled. Although I tried to shoo that baby cat away, he stubbornly refused to leave my yard.

To make matters much worse, a few days after my uninvited feline guest's arrival, I woke up at the crack of dawn to the sound of dogs barking. I stumbled to the window and rapped sharply on the glass, which usually causes my Jack Russell terriers to be quiet. Only this time their barking became louder and more frenzied. I muttered and grumbled as I climbed out of bed and wriggled into a sweatshirt.

I opened the back door groggily and yelled, "Harley and Dottie, hush!" hoping my disheveled appearance would be enough to silence them and I wouldn't actually have to leave the comfort of the kitchen and traipse up the dewy hill for a face-to-snout reprimand. Then I noticed Dottie had something in her mouth and was furiously shaking it. I sprinted toward her yelling, "Dottie, no!" because even from a distance I recognized her new chew toy as the homeless kitty.

By the time I got there, Dottie had placed the slobbery ball of orange fur on the ground and was looking at me with the same shame-faced expres-

Miraculously, that plucky kitten recovered from his near-death experience at the fangs of my dogs, so I christened him "Lazarus."

sion she wears when she's destroyed yet another dog bed. After shouting, "Bad, bad dog!" I scooped up the limp, barely breathing kitten and carried him into the house, thinking, *Every living thing deserves to have somebody with it when it dies,* and assuming I'd be burying the poor little thing within the hour.

Miraculously, that plucky kitten recovered, so I christened him "Lazarus." Within a week he was climbing trees and stalking butterflies and harassing me for fresh tuna. I couldn't help but spoil him, since I felt responsible for his near-death experience. More than once I found myself walking through the cat paraphernalia aisle at Target sheepishly piling things into my cart!

Lazarus even wormed his way into Harley's and Dottie's hearts and took to cuddling with them on chilly nights, purring away contently. Sometimes, when I watched him frolicking with them in the field behind my house, I was tempted to call out, "Lazarus, you idiot, those are the same mutts who tried to kill you!" But instead, I would just grin and think, *That silly cat has captivated us all.*

Lazarus the Cat

Almost a year from the day I met him, Lazarus wasn't at the back door waiting for his breakfast as usual, and I was immediately concerned. It wasn't like Lazarus to miss a meal. For the next several days, I went on long walks calling his name and even put up a "Lost Cat" sign in Puckett's, our local mom-and-pop grocery store.

About a week after Lazarus disappeared, a woman called because she had noticed the sign and recognized Lazarus as the cat she had seen run over by the car in front of her when she was driving her kids to school. She carefully explained that he hadn't suffered, because he'd been killed instantly. I told her that I really appreciated her call and was glad to know definitively what had happened to him. Then I hung up the phone, sat down heavily on my bed, and cried.

I still miss Lazarus. When he died, it was almost as if I had lost my pinky toe—not something you tend to appreciate, yet its absence leaves you noticeably off balance. I find myself often glancing up at the crook in the tree where he used to lounge and feel my heart skip a beat when I see another tabby that resembles him. Grieving for that cheeky critter has been a poignant reminder for me to be more appreciative of and attentive to all the little "kisses from God" that are woven into our lives.

This story is adapted from a chapter in *Stumbling Into Grace*, by Lisa Harper (Nashville: Thomas Nelson, 2011). This excerpt has been reprinted with permission from Thomas Nelson, Inc.

Infusion

ARLENE SALIBA

*L*ost in thought as I drove to the clinic, I tried to focus my attention on the road. Yet the basic desire for food was loud and persistent. I had grabbed leftovers to eat for lunch before starting work. The hunger pangs were so strong that I gave in and ate two cold eggrolls while driving.

Finally, I exited the highway. The clinic was only a mile away. Suddenly, I became conscious to the sound of breaking glass, scraping metal, and the explosion of air on my face. Opening my eyes, I found myself in the middle of the road. Both airbags in my van had deployed and both front windows were shattered. Something was trickling down the middle of my chest: BLOOD! What happened? Was anyone hurt? What did I hit?

A man came to my window to ask if I was hurt. I didn't think so, except for a cut on my chest. He said I had crossed the midline and hit another vehicle. It had rolled over on its side in the ditch and the driver had crawled out unhurt. The ambulance came and I was placed on a backboard with cervical spine precautions because I could not remember anything prior to the accident. All of a sudden I was no longer hungry. In fact I was nauseated. I protested the

"Trust in the Lord with all your heart, And lean not on your own understanding; In all your ways acknowledge Him, And He shall direct your paths"

PROVERBS 3: 5-6, NKJV.

cervical spine precautions but the ambulance crew thought it necessary especially with the development of nausea. They also had to consider a head injury.

After a CT scan and a few X-rays I was released with the diagnosis of a concussion but no broken bones. What a relief!

Over the next week I would have flashbacks of my first conscious moments after the accident. I relived the sounds of breaking glass, scraping metal and the bursting of the airbags. Sleep was fitful during those nights.

One particular night, I lay awake for a long time. The sounds played back in my head once more. The awful thought of what could have been brought fear to my heart: I could have killed or maimed the other driver. I could have been injured much more than I was. What would happen to my family if I was gone? Why didn't I make a sandwich that I could eat quickly instead of packing eggrolls, rice, and vegetables? Was there something that I could have done to prevent the accident?

In the darkness I prayed. "Forgive me, Lord, for not taking care of my body before taking care of others. This is such a bad time to have this accident. Our family cannot af-

Over the next week I would have flashbacks of my first conscious moments after the accident. I relived the sounds of breaking glass, scraping metal and the bursting of the airbags. Sleep was fitful during those nights.

ford another car payment at this time. At least the van was already paid for. How is this a fulfillment of your Word in Jeremiah's writings for peace and hope? These flashbacks
are not peaceful and the pending economic burden
of another car payment is far from hopeful. What
lesson can I learn from this experience?"

Slowly infusing from the top of my head
to the bottom of my feet came the answer.
Absolute peace enveloped my being like I
have never felt before. Then the message:
"My child, this is not about what you have
or have not done. This is not about you at all.
Don't you know that the devil is after your soul? The time is not yet. This is between him
and me. There is still plenty you can do for me."

Reassured that the fight was not mine, I drifted into sleep once more, never more to
be disturbed by flashbacks.

*"Trust in the Lord with all your heart, And lean not on your own understanding; In all
your ways acknowledge Him, And He shall direct your paths" (Proverbs 3: 5-6, NKJV).*

A Girl's Wish, A Woman's Existence

SHAMETA WEBB

$\mathcal{A}$s a little girl, she often imagined what it would be like to be that superstar she always dreamed of being. "I could be a famous singer," she said as she stood in the mirror with her hairbrush in her hand. "I also want to be an actress and a model," she joyously imagined in her head. She believed that she could be whatever she wanted to one day.

Growing up, self-doubt and insecurities began to enter her mind as she started questioning her appearance. "Why is my nose shaped this way?" and "Why can't I be a little bit shorter, because I'm too tall?" she asked herself. She doubted her abilities to do certain things even while in the midst of others. The television and magazines only added to her insecurities at times, as she constantly saw the perfect looking people gracing the covers and smiling as if they had everything all together.

Growing up, self doubt and insecurities began to enter her mind as she started questioning her appearance. "Why is my nose shaped this way?" and "Why can't I be a little bit shorter, because I'm too tall?" she asked herself.

"I know I'm beautiful, but there are just some things I would change if I could," she said. People always told her that she was pretty and she knew it also, but she just didn't always feel that way inside.

As this little girl got older and years passed by, she began to have a different outlook about herself and her life. She started to develop a closer relationship with God and the opinions of others didn't seem to matter as much anymore. She started studying God's Word and seeking his guidance and direction in her life. The closer she became with God, the more she understood the things he revealed to her. Her beauty became radiant to those she came in contact with. Her personality and presence revealed the love of God as she sought oneness with him more and more each day.

No longer did self-doubt and insecurities trouble her mind, because she became confident in the woman that God had made her. It was no longer about image or what she thought she should or shouldn't look like. Changing lives and helping others outweighed any of the superficial things that had seemed to matter to her before.

As a woman, God had given her that inner strength to conquer anything that came her way. Her words became so eloquent, but yet so powerful. Her beauty radiated both inside and out while captivating the attention of those that needed it the most. The love of God and the spirit of God had definitely replaced the self-doubt that had lingered in her mind as a young girl growing up.

"I will praise thee; for I am fearfully and wonderfully made: marvelous are thy works; and that my soul knoweth right well" PSALMS 139:14, KJV.

"Women are created special by God," she said to herself, as this became apparent to her more and more. "They're so strong, but yet so fragile; taking on different roles in life. They're required to keep going because there are so many people that depend on them. In their own pain and sorrow, they have to be there to stand for others who look to them for guidance. A woman's job is never complete. God knew this beforehand, that's why he created us so special and unique."

Father, I pray for all the young girls, young ladies, and women out there who are battling with self-esteem and self-worth issues. Please touch their hearts and minds and reveal to them your love as they begin to love themselves. Let them know that no matter what they go through and experience, no matter what people say about them, they are precious to you and worth more than anyone could ever put in words.

In Jesus' name, AMEN.

Trust

CHERYL MOSELEY

As I entered the departure gate, tears rolling down my face, I turned and waved goodbye to my two best friends. Everything I owned was either packed in my suitcase, somewhere in storage, or in a container crossing the Atlantic. I was leaving my home, my country, my friends and my family to go to a strange and lonely place. Three months before, my husband had travelled ahead of the family to the United States to begin a course of study for ministry. The only thing I was looking forward to was seeing him again.

For two years we had been praying and searching to know God's will for our lives. We felt sure that God had led us to this place, but now as I left home and friends, it seemed so hard. My security was gone; I was out of my comfort zone.

The next few months became very discouraging as all my hopes and dreams for this new adventure seemed lost. It felt like everything was going wrong and I questioned whether God really had been leading us in this direction. One thing that seemed to go wrong was selling our home. I felt sure that if this move was God's will he would sell our home immediately, without any problems. We needed to sell in order to finance the study and living expenses for the next three years. We faced many

This was a turning point for me; it seemed God was speaking to me again. It reminded me that I had stopped leaning upon him and wasn't trusting in him.

difficulties, lost thousands due to the failing economy, had buyers pull out at various stages and eventually had to leave our country without having secured a sale.

I had great plans for my children and was determined to see them back in Christian education again. That was not to be. The differences between the schooling system of our new home and that of our own country made it very difficult for the children to continue in school. I decided to home school my children despite having no experience in teaching whatsoever. This also meant putting my own plans aside so I could be home with my children.

Among other trials I became very discouraged with my friends back home. I had no e-mails or phone calls for weeks, maybe months after I arrived. I knew they were busy but all I needed was a friendly voice, someone interested in how I was doing, and someone who missed me. It seemed that now that I was gone they had forgotten me; at least that was what I told myself. My emotions took control and I allowed wrong thinking to dominate my life. "Why did we come here?" I kept asking myself. I felt God had deserted me.

Early on in our experience we kept coming across two verses that particularly encouraged us. They are found in Proverbs 3:5-6: *"Trust in the Lord with all your heart, And lean not on your own understanding; In all your ways acknowledge Him and He will direct your paths" (NKJV)*. One day, when I was feeling particularly low, my husband came home with a bunch of flowers to lift my spirits and two little cards from a Christian bookstore. One had my name written on it and the other had his name. Underneath each name was a text.

a text. My card had Proverbs 3:5 and yes, you've guessed it, his card had Proverbs 3:6! Amazing! This was a turning point for me; it seemed God was speaking to me again. It reminded me that I had stopped leaning upon him and wasn't trusting in him. I remembered all the ways in which God had led us here. Again I turned my life over to him, realizing that the only way I was going to get through was to trust. It's the best decision I have ever made.

Trusting my life to him has bought me peace and happiness in this place. God has answered many prayers and our whole family's experience in the United States has been truly amazing. We love living here! I feel closer to God and to my family through this experience. We only have a short time left in this place, and I know my tears will be greater leaving here than they were leaving home three years ago.

I made a decision that turned my experience around. I made a choice to trust.

Exposed

NONI BETH GIBBS

$\mathcal{S}$weetie, would you please have the kids pick up the trash in the yard?" my husband asked, getting in the van to go to work. I groaned and nodded. They had been at it again, throwing stuff out the second-story window. Bottles, papers, and even a book littered the thin layer of snow. I sighed again.

"Come on kids," I called. "Dad says to pick up the trash. Hurry or you'll be late for school. And stop throwing things out the window—I don't care if it's for science or not!"

"But it's cold," they whined, almost in unison.

"Maybe so," I shot back, "but you won't like cleaning it any better when it's 40 below."

As winter had increased its hold on the chilly northland where we lived, having moved from California, I had quickly learned that the snowfall itself was not the biggest problem. The brutal winds drove the snow across the prairie, where it collected into huge drifts. The same bushes that sheltered our yard also built up drifts, including a gigantic wave of snow along the edge of the driveway—complete with a curl on top. Pretty soon, even our drifts had drifts.

Still the naughty and short-sighted children continued to throw things out the window,

"I have blotted out, as a thick cloud, your transgressions, and like a cloud, your sins; return to Me, for I have redeemed you"

ISAIAH 44:22, NKJV.

trusting the snow and wind to hide the evidence. And so it did, layer upon layer, for about four months. Even a seemingly endless winter must come to an end, and at long last the trees lost their last few leaves, making way for new growth.

Temperatures rose above freezing, and the mountains of snow began to shrink. As the layers melted, the full mess of winter came into full view. It wasn't all the children. Trash had blown in from miles around, riding the swirling currents of many vicious storms before coming to rest on our property.

But though the three of them tried, there was no blaming Canada and the northerlies for the distinct piles under the upstairs windows. Pens, pencils, paper...they could almost have started a school down there.

As the snow continued to melt, every single thing they thought was so well hidden came into full view. Every secret relentlessly came to light; even the light bulbs they believed were gone forever. It took a massive effort on all our parts to get the yard cleaned up and looking decent again, and more than once I heard, "I wish we hadn't thrown this stuff all around."

The naughty and short-sighted children continued to throw things out the window, trusting the snow and wind to hide the evidence. And so it did, layer upon layer, for about four months.

So often we think we can hide the evil in our own hearts. With a thick coating of "snow" on the outside, we may appear to be just fine, even righteous. Only God knows for sure what is really underneath our protective layers—all those hidden sins that stand between us and an intimate relationship with our Creator.

When he turns the heat up, our sins are exposed. As uncomfortable as that is, he can't get rid of them till they're out in the open. And no matter how long it takes, God never runs out of patience with cleaning our hearts, time and time again.

What are you holding onto? What is keeping you from a joyous friendship with God? Let go of it. Give it to him. He has faithfully promised, *"I have blotted out, as a thick cloud, your transgressions, and like a cloud, your sins; return to Me, for I have redeemed you" (Isaiah 44:22, NKJV).*

You and I belong to him. He bought us, he forgave us, and he will cleanse us.

The Wiggly One

JANET SCHLUNT

People were gathering in the boarding area for the cross-country flight from Chicago to Portland. Southwest Airlines has open seating. I wanted to be early in line for my boarding section so I could get a choice seat near the front. That would enable me to be one of the first up the jet way. It was then I noticed the young mother with her toddler and infant. "Nobody is going to want to sit next to that wiggly boy," I thought to myself. "I'm traveling alone. I could do it. I might even be able to help the lady."

Sure enough, no one had chosen the aisle seat by the threesome. "May I sit here?" I requested. We exchanged a few pleasantries after which I suggested that she let me hold her sleeping darling while she attended to the wiggly one. Her treasure was gratefully handed over.

It was interesting to watch how the mother entertained her young son with creative drawings and tiny toys brought along for the purpose. "Are you a school teacher?" I asked. "Yes," she answered. "But I'm not working while my children are young." The little boy was well-behaved, but constantly moving. If she had had to hold the baby on her lap and entertain the

"Do not withhold good from those who deserve it when it's in your power to help them"

PROVERBS 3:27, NLT.

wiggly one it would have been much more difficult. I mentally recalled some of my own journeys with wiggly ones on my lap, especially the day my own toddler cried the entire trip from Chicago to Florida, which was something of a nightmare. At least neither of these children was crying or being difficult.

The sleeping baby seemed to get heavier as time went on. The book I had planned to read remained in my bag under the seat. Sleepiness overtook me for a short while. Then we could see the snow on Mt. Hood, and I knew the flight would soon end. Finally the wiggly one slept. The mother relaxed as we commented on how it so often happens that just before landing time a child will finally drop off to sleep. The baby sister had slept all the way across the country. Now she opened her big blue eyes and smiled at me, unafraid. Then it was my turn to play little games with her.

Placing one hand over my face and not making a sound, I revealed a little bit of my face by moving one finger at a time. Then all at once my hand came away and we both smiled with delight. This was repeated several times, always with the same result. How easy it was to entertain this contented baby!

We exchanged a few pleasantries after which I suggested that she let me hold her sleeping darling while she attended to the wiggly one. Her treasure was gratefully handed over.

I offered to help the children into their stroller on the jet way, but the mother assured me she would wait until the plane cleared of passengers and she could manage quite well on her own.

I was still one of the early ones off the plane. In the terminal stood a young father waiting for his family to return from baby's first visit to far away grandparents. He was easily identified from his wife's description. As I passed him I smiled and lifted up a prayer for God's blessing on this lovely young family.

"Do not withhold good from those who deserve it when it's in your power to help them" (Proverbs 3:27, NLT).

Wake up!

ASHLEY TARDIF

eep, beep, beep-beep, beep-beep…

The imposing alarm clock brought my senses to life. In a sleepy stupor, I squinted over at the clock. How dare it say 6:30 AM! Could I really have slept the entire night? How could morning have come so quickly? Shutting my eyes against the unrecognized miracle of another day, I rested my head back on the pillow. *Just a few more minutes of peace,* I thought. *Then I will get up and running for the day. I'll merely close my eyes and relax; forget about all the demands of today. And I won't fall asleep. I won't fall asleep….*

What seemed several minutes later, I startled awake. With horror, I beheld the clock, now displaying a prominent 7:35 AM. What had I done? Oh, *why* had I fallen back asleep! Chiding myself for not heading to bed at a decent hour the night before, I threw back the blankets and hurried to dress and prepare for the day.

"My voice You shall hear in the morning, O LORD; In the morning I will direct it to You, And I will look up"

PSALM 5:3, NKJV.

The indifferent altering of the clock's digits angered me while I scrambled to make myself presentable. There was so much to do, in so little time! My mind began involuntarily reciting the mental list of tasks that I needed to accomplish before the sun set that evening.

With a frown, I dashed to the kitchen for a bite of breakfast. Automatically bowing my head to thank God for my food, I realized I had neglected morning devotions - again. Guiltily, I pretended that God "understood" while I thrust into his hands my list of requests for the day.

I had thrown away the opportunity to begin my day seeking God's guidance. My 6:30 AM denial had set me up for a miserable day.

Contrast that, with this…

Feeling rested and rejuvenated from my night's rest, I awoke to the quiet of early morning. I silently slipped out of bed and down the hall to the living room sofa, where my Bible was waiting for me. Darkness dissipated as a nearby lamp illuminated the room. Reading my Bible and talking with my Father in the silence that surrounded me, I renewed my trust in him. The first rays of sunlight pierced the sky as I arose from my refuge, empowered for the daily battles ahead.

I felt prepared this time; ready for anything. Since I had spent time to pour out my heart's burdens to God, I didn't make the mistake of dumping them on others. Because I had paused to recommit myself to him, I could better trust

What seemed several minutes later, I startled awake. With horror, I beheld the clock, now displaying a prominent 7:35 AM. What had I done? Oh, why had I fallen back asleep!

God to help me through any obstruction in my path.

God longs to spend time with us each day. He eagerly waits for us to come to him and be filled with his presence. Of course, the devil doesn't want this to happen; he aims to keep us from God's presence in any way he can. He can't stand it when we want God's blessing more than an extra hour of sleep. He knows that those who immerse themselves in God's Word are difficult to subdue. So he fights to keep us slothful, not wanting us to recognize the power that is ours when we are filled with Jesus. The battle for time with God is a difficult one, but when we are victorious in the first battle of each day, the other battles that ensue are much easier to overcome.

By setting aside time for God each day, you are showing others who is most important in your life. And you can declare with the psalmist David: *"My voice You shall hear in the morning, O LORD; In the morning I will direct it to You, And I will look up" (Psalm 5:3, NKJV).*

Gardening 101

PATRICIA BODI

In early June, after a cold Michigan spring, my apartment complex gave me an offer I couldn't refuse – a free garden space. Being a "city girl," my only gardening experience was roses and tomatoes in pots on my patio and flowers around the perimeter of my condo. I didn't even bother to read how to plant a garden. I just went and purchased plants at a greenhouse. Even at that I failed, since I wouldn't listen when my friend told me I was getting enough tomatoes for the entire church! I went ahead and bought what I thought was a flat of 12 tomato plants which turned out to be 42! The mosquitoes were so bad that I just grabbed a few plants, paid for them, and took them home.

Now it was time to get them into the ground. I looked around the house for whatever I could find to dig some holes in which to put my precious tomato plants. I used a handy little kitchen gadget – don't laugh – it worked.

As I looked at my finished garden space and compared it to others, I couldn't help being embarrassed at my rudimentary attempts.

Now the serious part of gardening—watering! We were told to use the water from a nearby creek, but no one cut a path down there so that was impossible. I had to resort to lugging gallons of water from the outdoor spigot at the closest apartment building. It didn't help that I had plenty of company lugging water. I mean, does any of them have herniated discs, L3-4, L4-5 and Klippel–Feil syndrome in their cervical spine, carpal tunnel in both their wrists, and not even one good knee?!

I decided I couldn't afford forty-two tomato cages, so I again improvised—dowel rods at 29 cents each. As I looked at my finished garden space and compared it to others, I couldn't help being embarrassed at my rudimentary attempts. Other garden spaces appeared very geometric, sort of like they used a yardstick. Their plants were in a straight line! Some had built up mounds, had mulch and straw and lattice-type frames for their plants to climb. I was outclassed before I got started.

I learned from my neighboring plots, by observing what my fellow gardeners did, and talking to them. I did some mulching, too, and learned that weeding was a worse job than the watering, and like watering, it had to be done every day, too. My garden was beginning to look positively beautiful to me, anyhow. I got some compliments from my neighbors. Now I couldn't straighten up my rows, but was relieved when someone observed that my rows were perfect diagonally! Maybe I was ready for prime time gardening

Then the woodchucks came and feasted on our gardens while we slept. I still don't know how to get rid of them!

What lessons did I learn from gardening? I took pride in the fact that because of me, these plants were actually growing. When I used a little introspection, I realized my life kind of paralleled my gardening attempt. While I had no clear plan when I started, I learned as I went along, borrowed, and adopted ideas from others. If it weren't for other individuals in my life, I never would have made as significant a contribution as I had made. And the Master Gardener kept on watering and weeding even when I seemed distant and unapproachable. He was watching me grow.

What happened next surprised even me. After I got my garden looking good, I'd found myself weeding the garden spaces on either side of mine when the owners didn't do it. After all, the weeds might "jump" over into my space, I told myself. Isn't that a lot like my life—always trying to help others even when they don't ask or maybe even care? What are those fancy buzz words? —co-dependent, enabler? Yeah, gardening is a lot like life.

How does your garden look? Are your plants in nice straight rows? Are you weeding other's spaces? Is the Lord watering and weeding even when you are careless and nonchalant about your Christian experience?

Waiting for God

L Y L A N S H E P H E R D F I T Z G E R A L D

The morning air was fresh and crisp as I sat in the rocking chair on the lodge porch at the women's retreat. Fog hovered over the valley the same way sadness and grief lingered over my heart. The loss of my loving husband to cancer still consumed me, even after three years. Friends reminded me that I must get on with my life—but "get on" to where? I felt lost and very alone.

My prayers had focused on a home, the one John and I had planned to build before his illness. Just a log cabin on our farm, but a place of my own, my first true home. Not a rental house or either of our parents' homes, but my own. Once again I poured out my heart to my heavenly Father, and then sat quietly waiting. The psalmist's admonitions to "wait patiently upon the Lord" must have been written for me. It can be uncomfortable to sit in his presence, just waiting. But practice has taught me that this is the time when my faith, courage, and strength are renewed.

Never have I been disappointed when I spend time with him. This morning was no exception. His presence filled the air around

The loss of my loving husband to cancer still consumed me, even after three years. Friends reminded me that I must get on with my life—but "get on to where?" I felt lost and very alone.

me, and his voice reached into my heart. "I will give you a home for hurting hearts—a place of healing."

My spirit lifted like the fog in the valley. Sharing the promise with my special church "sistas" and friends doubled my joy.

Before his death, John and I had discussed developing a portion of the farm into a small subdivision and selling the lots to friends so we could finance our log cabin. Now I felt confident that this was the right decision and could hardly wait to see what God would do. Plans took shape quickly and amazing people stepped forward to help. An engineer friend offered to design the subdivision and help submit plans to the authorities. A contractor who came to talk about a gate became the perfect choice to install the road and utilities. Another friend helped design the entrance and a huge entry gate. A woman I had worked with years ago attended church with a builder who specializes in log homes.

Everything fell into place and moved quickly; then disaster struck. Land prices fell, and no one was able to purchase the lots at the established prices. The historical significance of the property was questioned, resulting in months of delays in construction. The county's use of a small strip of adjoining property had changed, making potential buyers uneasy about security.

I'm still not sure when or how my home will be built. But one thing is certain — I must step out in faith, trusting him.

Property tax appraisals had to be appealed. And, all the while, the interest on the bank loan continued to grow.

How could this happen? The development had been dedicated to God—for his glory! How could he allow things to get so out of control? Wait! Is he in control—or have I taken over? I suddenly realized that I had been too busy to spend time with my Friend. How could I not see that I had strayed from his plan? Much time has been spent asking for his forgiveness and then waiting, waiting, waiting for him. I could almost hear him sadly whisper, "Girlie, you're just getting too big for your britches."

Now we are back to the original plan—his plan. Keep it simple. Make it affordable for the people who need to be here. Trust him to provide for my needs. I'm still not sure when or how my home will be built. But one thing is certain—I must step out in faith, trusting him. I must allow my faith to grow by spending time with him—as I would any true friend. Sit in his presence—perhaps even climb up onto his lap and rest my head on his chest. What divine peace and security! It's all the home I could ever hope for.

Walk On

LAURA BRADFORD

The autumn day was dark, with clouds hanging heavily over our valley and dry wind pummeling everything in its path. I sat indoors, monitoring the skies every few minutes, longing for fair weather so I could take my daily walk. Sun and exercise seemed as if they'd be the perfect remedies for my aching body and melancholic mood.

The responsibilities of handling Dad's funeral had left me tense and exhausted. As I wrote out checks to the mortuary, the florist, and the cemetery, I was flooded with memories of my own husband's passing only four years earlier. Here I was again, laboring alone over the ugly details of death. It took what little strength I had to hold onto Jesus. But I refused to weep since I knew my loved ones' souls were safe.

About an hour before sunset, I determined I'd take a walk regardless of the dark, blustery conditions. Since I had the funeral bills to mail, I planned to walk only a few blocks to our local post office, then return home.

"He will wipe every tear from their eyes, and there will be no more death or sorrow or crying or pain. All these things are gone forever"

REVELATION 21:4, NLT.

As I fought against the wind, I felt as though my legs were carrying the heaviness of my heart. But the busy atmosphere at the post office brought some welcome relief. Just seeing people and say-

223

ing hellos helped to lift my mood. After mailing the bills, I started toward home, but sensed the Lord prompting me, "Go further—along your regular route."

I groaned.

Normally, I'd walk a three-mile circular route, up a hill and down again. But my usual energies were gone, especially with the wind fighting me every step of the way. After taking a few minutes to stare longingly in the direction of home, I turned around and surrendered my will to the Spirit's guidance.

Trudging away from the post office, I started up the hill along a quiet lane. But it was too quiet. The silence, the gray skies, and the effort of climbing all combined to overwhelm me. Long-overdue tears began rolling down my cheeks. Afraid someone might see me, I said, "Lord, why did you ask me walk farther? You knew it would be too much. Can't I just go home?"

"But, I have a gift for you," I sensed him telling me.

That aroused my curiosity! I dried my eyes and forced my limp legs to make the steep climb to the halfway point of my usual walking route.

As I rounded a corner, I saw my gift! Low-hanging clouds were departing, leaving a band of blue just above the western horizon. Within seconds, the setting sun dipped down to peek at me from under the clouds. Warm rays kissed my face, while rose-colored light streamed across the mountainsides and down our long valley. They were like beams of hope penetrating my gloom and reviving my strength. I quickened my pace as I walked on, thanking God profusely for this perfect gift.

Just as I'd turned west to face the brightness, a car pulled up beside me. To my surprise, my best friend hopped out. "Mind if I walk with you for a few blocks?" she asked. "I don't want to miss the sunshine."

"Come on," I invited. "This is great!"

She ended up walking me all the way home as we "oohed" and "aahed" over a landscape bathed in shifting rays of pink and golden light. Her friendship, coupled with the glorious evening, turned my focus forward, to a joyous time when we'll all be together, with no more tears ... forever.

God knew just what I needed to lift my lonely, grieving heart—a reminder of eternal hope and the company of a good friend.

Bonded by Wounds

MONICA AMES

One bright spring morning when I was just sixteen years old, I grabbed my ten-speed bike and rode over to my friend Carly's house for a visit. Carly and I liked to sit at the small table in the corner of her dad's kitchen and sip peppermint tea from fancy cups, imagining that we were grown up ladies at some fashionable café in Paris.

We chatted the morning away as the sun rose higher in the sky. What started out as typical teenage girl talk soon took a sharp turn and drifted into more serious topics. I knew it had not been easy for Carly since her Mom had left, but I had no idea what she was going through.

Carly started opening up and sharing things that normally she had kept hidden inside. Soon I was also sharing deep hurts that were close to my heart. Before long we were both in tears. I leaned over and wrapped my arm around Carly's shoulders and then we hugged each other while we cried. Amidst our sobs we heard a noise at the window. It was her faithful golden retriever, Jack, looking at us with big dark questioning eyes, wondering what was the matter. "Just look at us! We're a mess," Carly exclaimed.

Before long we were both in tears. I leaned over and wrapped my arm around Carly's shoulders and then we hugged each other while we cried.

Then we sat back blinking away the tears and burst

into laughter together. The rest of the morning consisted of more laughter and tears. As I rode home later that day breathing in the fresh spring air, life seemed different somehow. The problems I faced were just the same but my outlook had changed. I now had a friend who understood and cared. It was a healing relationship for both Carly and me. Because of that time we shared I was able to help Carly get to know the Bible and Jesus Christ. I gave her several texts to consider, but as time went by she moved and we lost contact.

Years later when I was in college I received an unexpected call at about 3 AM. There was a small timid voice on the other side of the line. It was Carly. We were about 700 miles apart and it had been quite some time since we had spoken, but I quickly woke up with excitement in just hearing her voice again.

Carly told me that her life had become unbearable and I was the only person she wanted to talk to. She was in a dangerous relationship that she needed to get out of. It thrilled my heart to hear that Carly had saved all the Scriptures that we had gone over together and

"Surely he took up our pain and bore our suffering, yet we considered him punished by God, stricken by him, and afflicted. But he was pierced for our transgressions, he was crushed for our iniquities; the punishment that brought us peace was on him, and by his wounds we are healed" ISAIAH 53:4-5, NIV.

she still treasured them. I was able to encourage and pray with her so she could take a stand for what was right. Then I sent her the prettiest, most uplifting card I could find.

I'm so glad Jesus brought Carly into my life. The love and caring of our friends can go a long way in lifting our spirits. Being a friend to someone brightens our own days, but the friendship we can share with Jesus is infinitely greater than what we can experience with any other person. Just as Carly and I were able to share our hurts, so Jesus has borne all the weight of sin upon himself and longs to share that message with us. Of course, Christ wants to hear our hurts and pains, and has a deeper empathy than any human being could ever provide. He is there for us in the darkness of every night and the wee hours of every morning. He understands our feelings even more than we can understand them ourselves. He's waiting at our kitchen table, or any other place we might happen to be, for us to pour out our hearts and share our joys with him. Why not give him a try?

One of My Favorite Gifts

Lisa Clouzet

Christmas can be such a joyful time, a time when love is shared from one heart to another. It can also be a very lonely time. It was the beginning of a Christmas season, while doing chaplaincy visitation in an assisted care facility, when I met Marva—an amazing woman who was struggling with the holiday blues. She had suffered a stroke which left her partially paralyzed on her right side. Her children were about my age and busy with their own lives. Not wanting to add to their burdens, she had chosen to live in a small room which she had furnished with the bare necessities and a picture or two. Marva's life at that point was routine and uneventful, except for the occasional visit from a family member or friend.

That December day, I asked Marva what she enjoyed most about Christmas. She seemed to gain energy as she recalled Christmases past and all the traditional festivities which she had enjoyed around her family. Her eyes glistened as she described exploring the neighborhood's Christmas lights and decorations. She reminisced as though she would never again experience that pleasure. Before I had really thought about it—about how busy I was, about how many Christmas preparation items I had on my list, about how little time I

Before I had really thought about it I was inviting Marva to go on an outing to explore the Christmas lights! She was surprised and excited and accepted my offer.

had to get ready—I was inviting Marva to go on an outing to explore the Christmas lights! She was surprised and excited and accepted my offer.

The day came for our outing. It had been a long day and I felt low in energy as I dragged myself to the assisted care center. I was energized when I saw Marva, all dressed up and waiting to go on her adventure. Her eyes sparkled, her face glowed, and she chattered like a school girl. For Marva, ordinary tasks took more time than usual. We donned her coat, ambled to my mini-van and then the fun began. We pulled and tugged and managed to get her up into the van and settled into her seat and seatbelt. After stowing her walker in the back seat, we were off!

We had gone less than a mile when Marva mentioned she was warm and would like to remove her coat. Normally that would not be a big deal. But removing her coat involved pulling over, wrestling her out of her jacket and back into her seatbelt. Marva and I laughed uncontrollably at the thought of what a show we were providing for passersby. It also provided good medicine for us!

The excitement of the evening grew as we passed by house after house decorated in bright lights and seasonal fare. After an hour of exploring, Marva was satisfied and ready to return to the place she called home. Knowing she seldom had the opportunity to leave the center, I asked her if there was anything else she would like to do while we were out. Her eyes lit up once again as she said she would love to stop somewhere and buy her favorite candy bar. Since she was allowed sweets in her diet, I pulled over at the next gas station. When I returned with two of her prized candy bars, she delightedly opened one and slowly ate it on the way back.

Marva shared with me the gift of appreciating people and relationships, and of treasuring the important moments in life. By responding to her love and her simple request, both of our lives were enriched and another memory made. She seized the moment and so did I.

Marva did not live to see another Christmas, as she passed away the following spring. I think of her as each holiday season rolls around. I try to look for gifts to share that money cannot buy. I also look for the extraordinary gifts in ordinary moments.

"In everything I did, I showed you that by this kind of hard work we must help the weak, remembering the words the Lord Jesus himself said: 'It is more blessed to give than to receive'" (Acts 20:35, NIV).

About the Authors

Sara Alsup has been teaching Bible studies for about fifteen years and speaks regularly as part of a spiritual retreat ministry.

Monica Ames is the VBS director at her church and also serves as a member of a women's ministry board.

Carla Baker serves as director of women's ministries in Silver Spring, Maryland. She previously lived near Fort Worth, Texas, where for eleven years she also served as director of women's ministries.

In 1996, **Gladys Joy! Bazemore** became a full-time literature evangelist in Georgia. She lives and works in Oklahoma.

Patricia Bodi is active in Women's Ministries in Michigan. Her passion is walking so she enjoys leading women in "Walking with Jesus" at retreats.

Laura L. Bradford's writings have been published in several inspirational anthologies compiled by *Guideposts*, *Chicken Soup for the Soul*, and *A Cup of Comfort*.

Dawn S. Brown and her family live in Orlando and are committed to living the CREATION Health principles.

Dorothy L. Brown served as a registered nurse for about thirty years, with most of her experience in mental health.

Alicia Bruxvoort describes herself as "a lover of Jesus Christ, a seeker of abundant life, and a freelance writer and speaker." She blogs daily at **www.AliciaBruxvoort.net.**

Lisa Clouzet serves as a chaplain and licensed counselor. She currently teaches in Berrien Springs, Michigan.

Joanne Cortes and her husband serve in pastoral ministry. She says that her main desire is to be a reflection of Jesus and share his love.

Terri Cruze is a nurse by trade and is the author of two books *Finding Peace in the Midst of Chaos* and *Joy for the Troubled Heart*.

Dorothy Davis is a retired elementary school teacher. She serves as a mentor for a Christian school in Gary, Indiana.

Lizbeth Fernandez is the mother of a beautiful girl who has Down Syndrome. She makes her home in Orlando.

Lylan Sherpherd Fitzgerald is a Licensed Massage Therapist who enjoys writing. She is active in Women's Ministries.

Ana Boudet Forman has taught religion to middle school students for more than twenty years. She enjoys reading; "deep, change the world" conversations, and Florida Gator football.

Delores Francois volunteers at a local community crisis organization as a helpline counselor and a rape response advocate.

Noni Beth Gibbs has written two books, *Malchus: Touched by Jesus*, and *Peter: Fisher of Men*. She lives in Montana with her husband, Jack, and their three adventuresome children.

Jenni Glass lives and writes in Overland Park, Kansas. She works in marketing and research for the local Chamber of Commerce.

Carmalita Green is a Registered Dietitian for the Montgomery County Health Department.

Linda Nordyke Hambleton is the author of *If Today is all I Have*.

Lisa Harper is a popular speaker and author of over a dozen books including *A Perfect Mess* and *Stumbling Into Grace*. Her style combines sound scriptural exposition with easy-to-relate to anecdotes and comedic wit. Visit her at **www.LisaHarper.net**.

Helen Heavirland teaches a writing class and has published more than 200 short pieces. Her latest book, *My Enemy, My Brother,* is a true story out of World War II which gives rise to hope.

Codi Jahn enjoys spending time with friends and family, traveling, and delicious food. She volunteers at a local high school where she coaches the varsity volleyball team.

Sharon Jallad is married and has two grown children. She is the co-owner and Executive Vice President of Accredited Surety and Casualty Company, Inc.

About the Authors

Dr. Lorraine James-Stiggers is an author, poet, avid reader, and motivational speaker who has traveled across America and abroad conducting workshops and seminars for churches, schools, and businesses.

Collene Kelly has written for the Indiana Conference Family Life Department, the Adventist Review, and the NAD Women's Ministry Department.

Mary Kendall makes her home in Columbia, Missouri where she enjoys writing and serving as a Dental Hygienist.

Patty Knittel enjoys writing, golf, reading, travel, and her cats. Her writing has appeared in various Christian magazines.

Betty Kossick is the author of *Beyond the Locked Door* and *Heart Ballads*. She has also served as a contributor to fourteen other books. Though she is in her 80s, she avidly continues as a freelance writer.

Stephanie Lind serves as Director for Healthy 100 Church Ministry & Business Development at Florida Hospital. In this role, she serves churches seeking to inspire, inform, and implement whole person health ministry in their communities.

Cynthia Mercer is a registered nurse living in Woodward, Oklahoma. She enjoys serving in full-time ministry along with her husband.

Frances Morford spent over thirty-five years serving in Africa with her husband. Her ministry work included teaching English and the Bible as well as typing, home economics, and health classes.

Cheryl Moseley lives in Berrien Springs, Michigan with her husband Andy and their children. She homeschools her children and studies psychology.

Mulenga Mundende makes her home in Kansas where she writes and serves as a registered ICU nurse.

Judith Newton writes a column for her local newspaper from a spiritual perspective. She also hosts a weekly radio spot on her church's Christian radio station.

Kimberly Quinnie has created Bible studies for the deaf and hard of hearing. She currently resides in South Korea, where she is a missionary English instructor and Bible teacher.

Eve Rusk makes her home in Boise, Idaho. She enjoys working with children's programs at her church.

Arlene Saliba currently teaches in the nursing program at Andrews University and works part-time as a family nurse practitioner.

Jamie Santa Cruz is an instructor of religion at Indiana University in South Bend, Indiana.

Janet Schlunt has served as a departmental secretary at a Michigan university and a secretary in the office of the president at Pacific Union College.

Ashley Tardif lives and writes in the great state of Maine. Her life's dream is to be a full-time missionary in Eastern Africa.

Jean Thomason has released numerous books, videos, and CDs for preschoolers. An accomplished singer, songwriter and performer, Jean communicates biblical truth through her character named Miss Patty Cake. For more, visit *www.MissPattyCake.com*.

Diane Thurber serves as assistant communication director and managing editor of The Lake Union Herald. Diane is also a sponsor of RMC Shepherdess, a ministry for pastors' wives.

Shameta Webb writes from Orlando, Florida where she has lived and worked in healthcare for the past ten years.

LEAD YOUR COMMUNITY
TO HEALTHY
LIVING
With C·R·E·A·T·I·O·N Health
Seminars, Books, & Resources

SEMINAR MATERIALS

INCLUDES ONLINE TRAINING

Leader Guide

Everything a leader needs to conduct this seminar successfully, including key questions to facilitate group discussion and PowerPoint™ presentations for each of the eight principles.

Participant Guide

A study guide with essential information from each of the eight lessons along with outlines, self assessments, and questions for people to fill-in as they follow along.

Small Group Kit

It's easy to lead a small group using the CREATION Health videos, the Small Group Leaders Guide and the Small Group Discussion Guide.

CREATION Health Resources

CREATION Health Discovery (Softcover)

CREATION Health Discovery takes the 8 essential principles of CREATION Health and melds them together to form the blueprint for the health we yearn for and the life we are intended to live.

CREATION Health Devotional (English) (Hardcover)

Stories change lives. Stories can inspire health and healing. In this devotional you will discover stories about experiencing God's grace in the tough times, God's delight in triumphant times, and God's presence in peaceful times. Based on the eight timeless principles of wellness: Choice, Rest, Environment, Activity, Trust, Interpersonal relationships, Outlook, Nutrition.

CREATION Health Devotional (Spanish) (Softcover)

CREATION Health Breakthrough (Hardcover)

Blending science and lifestyle recommendations, Monica Reed, MD, prescribes eight essentials that will help reverse harmful health habits and prevent disease. Discover how intentional choices, rest, environment, activity, trust, relationships, outlook, and nutrition can put a person on the road to wellness. Features a three-day total body rejuvenation therapy and four-phase life transformation plan.

The Love Fight (English)

Are you going to fight for love or against each other? In *The Love Fight*, Drs. Tony Ferretti and Peter Weiss address a new dichotomy: the clash between Achievers and Connectors. The authors illustrate how this common encounter can create a mutually satisfying relationship. Their expertise will walk you through the scrimmage between those who want to accomplish and those who want to relate.

CREATION Health Resources

Forgive To Live (English) (Hardcover)

In *Forgive to Live* Dr. Tibbits presents the scientifically proven steps for forgiveness – taken from the first clinical study of its kind conducted by Stanford University and Florida Hospital.

Forgive To Live (Spanish) (Softcover)

Forgive To Live Devotional (Hardcover)

In his powerful new devotional Dr. Dick Tibbits reveals the secret to forgiveness. This compassionate devotional is a stirring look at the true meaning of forgiveness. Each of the 56 spiritual insights includes motivational Scripture, an inspirational prayer, and two thought-provoking questions. The insights are designed to encourage your journey as you begin to *Forgive to Live*.

Forgive To Live Workbook (Softcover)

This interactive guide will show you how to forgive – insight by insight, step by step – in a workable plan that can effectively reduce your anger, improve your health, and put you in charge of your life again, no matter how deep your hurts.

Forgive To Live God's Way (Softcover)

Forgiveness is so important that our very lives depend on it. Churches teach us that we should forgive, but how do you actually learn to forgive? In this spiritual workbook noted author, psychologist, and ordained minister Dr. Dick Tibbits takes you step-by-step through an eight-week forgiveness format that is easy to understand and follow.

CREATION Health Resources

CREATION Health Discovery (Softcover)

CREATION Health Discovery takes the 8 essential principles of CREATION Health and melds them together to form the blueprint for the health we yearn for and the life we are intended to live.

CREATION Health Devotional (English) (Hardcover)

Stories change lives. Stories can inspire health and healing. In this devotional you will discover stories about experiencing God's grace in the tough times, God's delight in triumphant times, and God's presence in peaceful times. Based on the eight timeless principles of wellness: Choice, Rest, Environment, Activity, Trust, Interpersonal relationships, Outlook, Nutrition.

CREATION Health Devotional (Spanish) (Softcover)

CREATION Health Breakthrough (Hardcover)

Blending science and lifestyle recommendations, Monica Reed, MD, prescribes eight essentials that will help reverse harmful health habits and prevent disease. Discover how intentional choices, rest, environment, activity, trust, relationships, outlook, and nutrition can put a person on the road to wellness. Features a three-day total body rejuvenation therapy and four-phase life transformation plan.

The Love Fight (English)

Are you going to fight for love or against each other? In *The Love Fight*, Drs. Tony Ferretti and Peter Weiss address a new dichotomy: the clash between Achievers and Connectors. The authors illustrate how this common encounter can create a mutually satisfying relationship. Their expertise will walk you through the scrimmage between those who want to accomplish and those who want to relate.

CREATION Health Resources

Forgive To Live (English) (Hardcover)

In *Forgive to Live* Dr. Tibbits presents the scientifically proven steps for forgiveness – taken from the first clinical study of its kind conducted by Stanford University and Florida Hospital.

Forgive To Live (Spanish) (Softcover)

Forgive To Live Devotional (Hardcover)

In his powerful new devotional Dr. Dick Tibbits reveals the secret to forgiveness. This compassionate devotional is a stirring look at the true meaning of forgiveness. Each of the 56 spiritual insights includes motivational Scripture, an inspirational prayer, and two thought-provoking questions. The insights are designed to encourage your journey as you begin to *Forgive to Live*.

Forgive To Live Workbook (Softcover)

This interactive guide will show you how to forgive – insight by insight, step by step – in a workable plan that can effectively reduce your anger, improve your health, and put you in charge of your life again, no matter how deep your hurts.

Forgive To Live God's Way (Softcover)

Forgiveness is so important that our very lives depend on it. Churches teach us that we should forgive, but how do you actually learn to forgive? In this spiritual workbook noted author, psychologist, and ordained minister Dr. Dick Tibbits takes you step-by-step through an eight-week forgiveness format that is easy to understand and follow.

CREATION Health Resources

If Today Is All I Have (Softcover)

At its heart, Linda's captivating account chronicles the struggle to reconcile her three dreams of experiencing life as a "normal woman" with the tough realities of her medical condition. Her journey is punctuated with insights that are at times humorous, painful, provocative, and life-affirming.

SuperSized Kids (Hardcover)

In *SuperSized Kids*, Walt Larimore, MD, and Sherri Flynt, MPH, RD, LD, show how the mushrooming childhood obesity epidemic is destroying children's lives, draining family resources, and pushing America dangerously close to a total healthcare collapse – while also explaining, step by step, how parents can work to avert the coming crisis by taking control of the weight challenges facing every member of their family.

Pain Free For Life (Hardcover)

In *Pain Free For Life*, Scott C. Brady, MD, – founder of Florida Hospital's Brady Institute for Health – shares for the first time with the general public his dramatically successful solution for chronic back pain, Fibromyalgia, chronic headaches, Irritable bowel syndrome, and other "impossible to cure" pains. Dr. Brady leads pain-racked readers to a pain-free life using powerful mind-body-spirit strategies used at the Brady Institute – where more than 80 percent of his chronic-pain patients have achieved 80-100 percent pain relief within weeks.

Leadership in the Crucible of Work (Hardcover)

What is the First and Most Important Work of a Leader? (The answer may surprise you.) In *Leadership in the Crucible of Work*, noted speaker, poet, and college president Dr. Sandy Shugart takes readers on an unforgettable journey to the heart of what it means to become an authentic leader.

"Come near to God and he will come near to you..." – James 4:8, NIV

www.FloridaHospitalPublishing.com

www.Facebook.com/FloridaHospitalPublishing

C·R·E·A·T·I·O·N Health

LIFE GUIDE SERIES

8 Guides. 8 Principles. One Powerful Message.
Packed with fresh insights on abundant living.
For Individual Study and Small Group Use.

Perfect for churches, schools, universities, and faith-based businesses.